Contemporary's
NUMBER POWER

Geometry
ROBERT MITCHELL
& DONALD PRICKEL

Consultants:
Heiko Fredericks
Instructor
East San Diego Adult Center
San Diego, California

June Hays
Learning Laboratory Instructor
San Diego Centre City Center
San Diego, California

Project Editor:
Caren Van Slyke

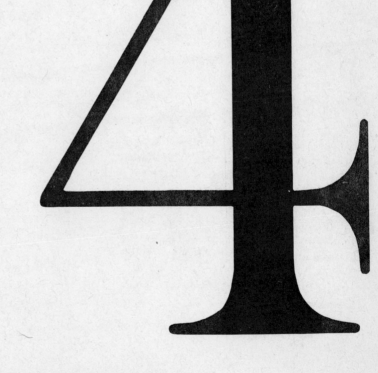

Contemporary Books, Inc.
Chicago

Published by Contemporary Books, Inc.
180 North Michigan Avenue, Chicago, Illinois 60601
International Standard Book Number: 0-8092-5583-9

Published simultaneously in Canada by
Beaverbooks, Ltd.
150 Lesmill Road
Don Mills, Ontario M3B 2T5
Canada

Production Editor: Debby Eisel

Illustrations: Ophelia Chambliss-Jones

TABLE OF CONTENTS

SOLID FIGURES

USING NUMBER POWER

TO THE STUDENT

Welcome to geometry:

Geometry is the study of the measurement and relationships of lines, angles, plane (flat) figures, and solid figures. Important topics from geometry include the study of angles and triangles and the study of distance, area, and volume. An understanding of these topics is necessary in many occupations. Also, geometry is a standard section on educational and vocational tests, including GED, college entrance, civil service, and military tests.

This workbook is designed to prepare you for taking a test and for pursuing further education or training that requires basic geometry. The first part of the book, BUILDING NUMBER POWER, provides step-by-step instruction in the fundamentals of geometry. This part is divided into four chapters. Each chapter begins with a skills inventory to help identify geometric skills you need work on. Each chapter ends with a final skills inventory to check your progress on newly acquired skills.

The second part of the book, USING NUMBER POWER, will give you a chance to apply geometric skills in more detail. These applications are fun and are examples of the use of geometry in everyday life.

To get the most out of your work, do each problem carefully and check each answer to make sure you are working accurately. An answer key is provided at the back of the book.

BUILDING NUMBER POWER

ANGLES

ANGLES SKILLS INVENTORY

This inventory will let you know what you need to work on in the ANGLES section of *Number Power: Geometry*.

Do all of the following problems that you can. There is no time limit. Work carefully and check all your answers.

Problems 1-3:   Write the symbol (letter name) that represents each angle below.

1. Symbol: _____

2. Symbol: _____

3. Symbol: _____

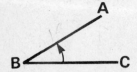

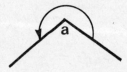

Problems 4 and 5:   Circle the letter of the correct multiple-choice response.

4. Angle ABC is a(n) _____ angle.
   a) acute
   b) right
   c) obtuse
   d) straight
   e) reflex

5. Angle RST is a(n) _____ angle.
   a) acute
   b) right
   c) obtuse
   d) straight
   e) reflex

6. Measure ∠ LMN.

   ∠ LMN = _____

7. Measure ∠ XYZ.

   ∠ XYZ = _____

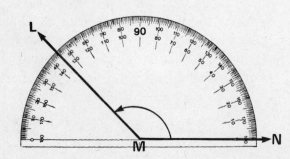

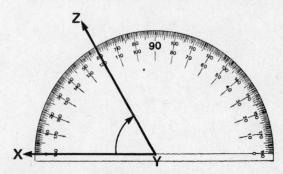

8. Using the protractor below, draw a 110° angle that opens counter-clockwise ⟩ .

9. Using the protractor below, draw a 75° angle that opens clockwise ⟨ .

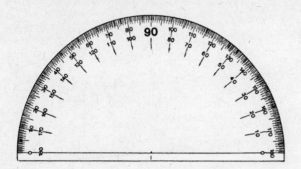

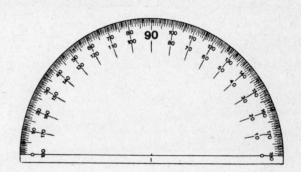

10. What is the value of ∠ GHI in the drawing below?

_____

11. In the drawing below, a brace makes a 37° angle with the cross beam. What is the value of the complementary angle that the brace makes with the upright beam?

_____

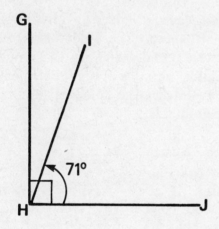

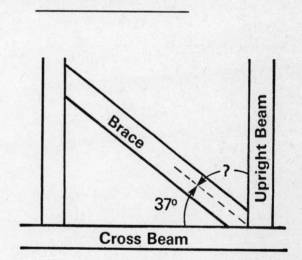

12. What is the complement of 14°?

_____

13. A fireplace hearth is designed to divide the corner angle (90°) of a room into two smaller angles. If the larger of the two complementary angles is 58°, what does the smaller angle measure?

_____

14. What is the value of ∠ ABC in the drawing below?

∠ ABC =_____

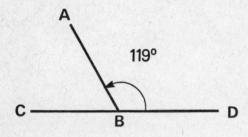

15. Oak Street intersects Twenty-second Avenue at an obtuse angle of 126°. What is the value of the acute angle at the intersection of Oak and Twenty-second?

_____

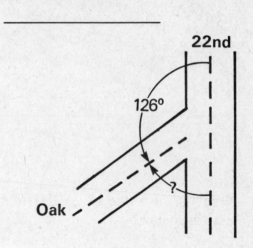

16. What is the supplement of 138°?

_____

17. Alan placed a ladder against the side of his house. The ladder makes an acute angle of 78° with the ground. What is the value of the supplementary angle that the ladder makes with the ground?

_____

18. What are the values of ∠ 2, ∠ 3, and ∠ 4 in the drawing below?

∠ 2 = _____

∠ 3 = _____

∠ 4 = _____

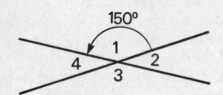

19. Lincoln Street intersects Howard Street at an acute angle of 25°. What are the values of the other angles at this intersection?

∠ a = _____

∠ b = _____

∠ c = _____

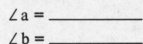
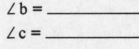
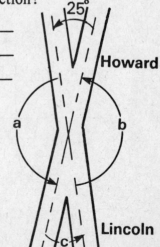

20. In the figure below there are seven unmeasured angles. Label each of these angles with its value.

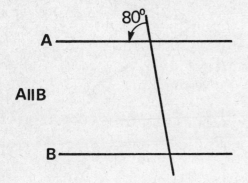

21. The Amtrak railroad tracks cross Elm and Pine streets as shown in the drawing below. Label each angle at both intersections with its value.

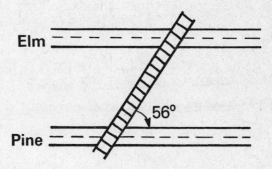

ANGLES INVENTORY CHART

Use this inventory to see what you already know about angles and what you need to work on. A passing score is 18 correct answers. Even if you have a passing score, circle the number of any problem that you miss, correct it, and turn to the practice page indicated.

Problem	Skill Area	Page
1	labeling angles	12
2	labeling angles	12
3	labeling angles	12
4	types of angles	10+11
5	types of angles	10+11
6	measuring angles	13+14
7	measuring angles	13+14
8	drawing angles	16
9	drawing angles	16
10	pairs of angles	18+19
11	pairs of angles: applying skills	20
12	pairs of angles	18+19
13	pairs of angles: applying skills	20
14	pairs of angles	18+19
15	pairs of angles: applying skills	20
16	pairs of angles	18+19
17	pairs of angles: applying skills	20
18	pairs of angles	18+19
19	pairs of angles: applying skills	20
20	parallel lines cut by transversal	22+23
21	parallel lines: applying skills	24

INTRODUCING ANGLES

An *angle* is formed when two lines meet at a point:

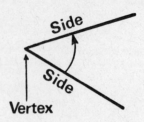

The lines that form the angle are called the *sides* of the angle.

The point where the lines meet is called the *vertex* of the angle.

The *size* of an angle depends only on the "opening" between its sides.

A larger angle has more "opening" than a smaller angle.

Angles can be very small

or very large.

Notice that an arc ⌒ is drawn to tell which of two possible angles is being indicated.

For example, ∠ might represent either ⟋ or ⟋

The arc identifies either the smaller "inside" angle or the larger "outside" angle.

Notice also that the size of an angle is not changed when an angle is turned or when the lengths of the sides are changed.

Each Angle Below Is the Same Size

Turning an angle does not change its size.

Changing the length of one or both sides of an angle does not change its size.

Circle the largest angle in each group of three angles below.

1.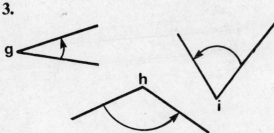

2.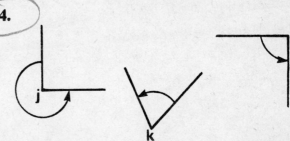

3.

4.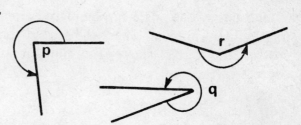

5.

6.

In each group of three angles below, circle the two equal angles.

7.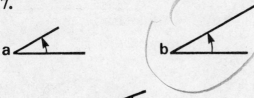

8.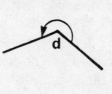

9.

10.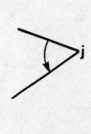

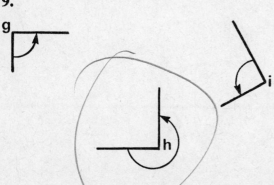

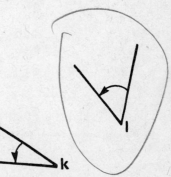

MEASUREMENT OF AN ANGLE

As you've seen, the size of an angle depends only on the "opening" between its sides. This "opening" is measured in units called "degrees." The symbol for "degrees" is "°". Thus "45 degrees" is written 45°. A larger angle has more degrees than a smaller angle.

Degrees can be thought of as parts of a circle. A whole circle is divided into 360 degrees.

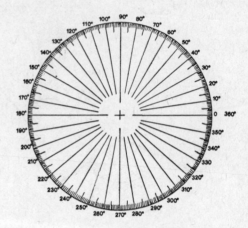

Thus, one degree is $\frac{1}{360}$ of a circle.

——————— 1°

The size of an angle is found by comparing the angle with a divided circle:

One side of the angle can be placed along the 0° line. The point where the second side crosses the circle shows the number of degrees in the angle.

A circle contains 360°.

EXAMPLE 1:   What is the size of the angle at the right?
One side of the angle is placed along the 0° line.
The second side crosses the circle at **80°.**

Answer: **The angle measures 80°.**

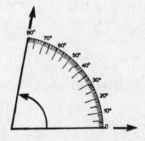

EXAMPLE 2:   A pie is cut into eight equal pieces. What angle do the straight sides of each piece make?

A whole pie is a circle. Since the pie is cut into eight equal pieces, each piece contains $\frac{1}{8}$ of the total degrees in a circle.

To find the number of degrees in each piece, divide 360° by 8:

Each piece = $\frac{360°}{8}$ = **45°**

Answer: **Each piece is cut at a 45° angle.**

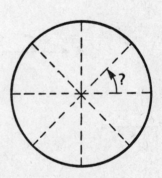

How many degrees are in each angle below? Write your answer on the line above the angle.

1. _____   2. _____   3. _____

Match each angle with its approximate size. Write the letter of the size in the answer space.
For reference, you may use the divided circle in Example 2 on the preceding page.

4. _____   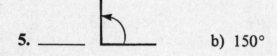   a) 180°

5. _____   b) 150°

6. _____   c) 210°

7. _____      d) 35°

8. _____   e) 90°

9. A whole pie is divided into twelve equal pieces. At what angle is each piece cut?

_____

10. A circular loaf of bread is to be divided into nine equal pieces. At what angle should each piece be cut?

_____

11. How many degrees are in one-fourth of a circle?

_____

12. How many degrees are in an angle that divides a circle into two equal parts?

_____

TYPES OF ANGLES

An angle is often named according to its size. Below are listed five types of angles with which you should become familiar.

Acute Angles

An *acute angle* measures more than 0° but less than 90°.

EXAMPLES:

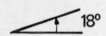 18°

 72°

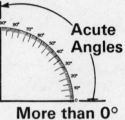

Less than 90°

Acute Angles

More than 0°

Right Angles

A *right angle* measures exactly 90°. A right angle is often indicated by placing a small square at its vertex.

EXAMPLES:

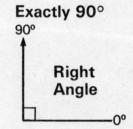

Exactly 90°

90°

Right Angle

0°

Note: Lines that meet at a right angle are called perpendicular lines. The symbol for perpendicular lines is ⊥.

Obtuse Angles

An *obtuse angle* measures more than 90° but less than 180°.

EXAMPLES: 160°   112°

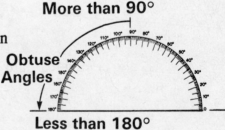

More than 90°

Obtuse Angles

Less than 180°

Straight Angles

A *straight angle* measures exactly 180°. A straight angle is the same as a straight line.

EXAMPLES:

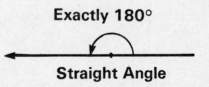

Exactly 180°

Straight Angle

Reflex Angles

A _reflex angle_ measures more than 180° but less than 360°.

EXAMPLES:

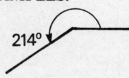

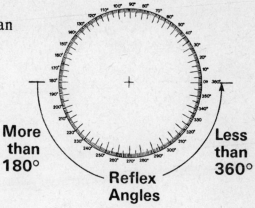

More than 180°   **Less than 360°**

Reflex Angles

Note: A reflex angle is the "outside" angle formed when two lines meet at a point.

Name each angle below: acute, right, obtuse, straight, or reflex.

1. _____

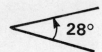

28°

2. _____

3. _____

150°

4. _____

180°

5. _____

310°

6. _____

88°

7. _____

131°

8. _____

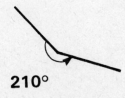

210°

9. _____

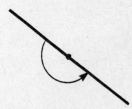

LABELING AN ANGLE

Angles are often labeled with letters or numbers. The symbol "∠" is commonly used to stand for the word "angle."

Two common labeling methods are shown below:

Labeling Methods   **Symbol**

1. An angle is often labeled with three letters: one letter is placed at the end of each side, and one is placed at the vertex.

   The letter placed at the vertex is called the *vertex letter*. The vertex letter is always written as the second of the three.
   Note: The angle at right can be written as ∠ABC or as ∠CBA.

1. By three letters

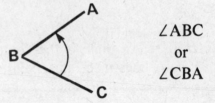

∠ABC
or
∠CBA

2. An angle can also be labeled with a vertex letter or number only. The vertex letter or number can be placed either on the outside or the inside of the angle.

   Outside of angle:

   Inside of angle:

2. By vertex letter or number.

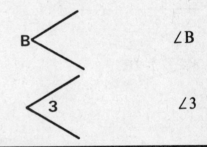

∠B

∠3

Write the symbol that represents each labeled angle below.

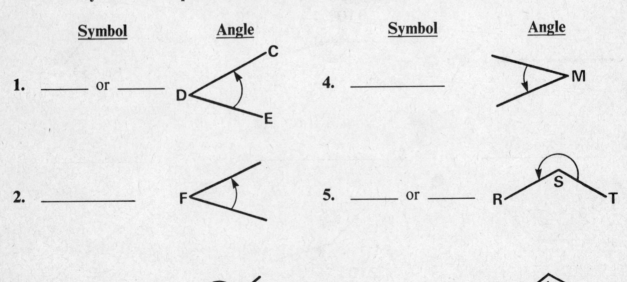

Symbol	Angle		Symbol	Angle
1. ____ or ____		**4.** _____		
2. _____		**5.** ____ or ____		
3. _____		**6.** _____		

MEASURING AN ANGLE WITH A PROTRACTOR

A *protractor* is a tool used for measuring and drawing angles. The most commonly used protractor is shaped like a half circle and can measure angles up to 180°. Carpenters, machinists, and others who read blueprints or plans use protractors in their work.

EXAMPLE: Use a protractor to measure angle RST to the right.

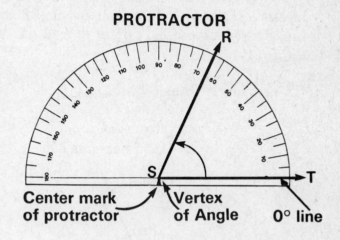

PROTRACTOR

Step 1. Place the center mark of the protractor at the vertex of the angle, and place the 0° line along one side (ST) of angle RST.

Step 2. Read the point where the second side (SR) crosses the protractor scale.

　　　If the side of the angle does not reach the protractor scale, extend the line so that the measurement can be read.

Center mark of protractor　Vertex of Angle　0° line

Answer: ∠RST = 65°

Note: A protractor is usually made of clear plastic. A protractor will be drawn for each angle you are asked to measure or to draw in this book.

Measure and name the type of each angle drawn below.

1. ∠ABC = _____
　　Type of Angle: _____

2. ∠DEF = _____
　　Type of Angle: _____

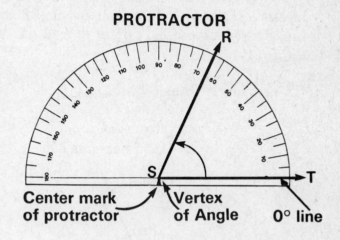

3. ∠XYZ = _____
　　Type of Angle: _____

4. ∠RST = _____
　　Type of Angle: _____

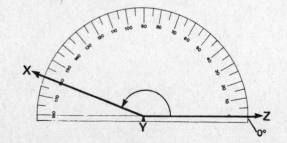

We can identify an angle by an arc that points either clockwise ⊂ or counterclockwise ⊃. So far in our study of angles, we have identified each angle as opening counterclockwise. However, many angles are easier to measure if we identify them as opening in a clockwise direction.

   To make measuring easier, a protractor usually has two scales. The inside scale is used to measure angles that open counterclockwise, and the outside scale is used to measure angles that open clockwise. Be careful to read the correct scale for the angle you are measuring.

EXAMPLE 1: Angle LMN is an acute angle that opens counterclockwise.

   ∠ LMN measures 65°

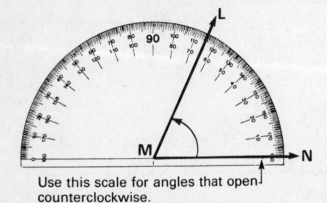

Use this scale for angles that open counterclockwise.

EXAMPLE 2: Angle ABC is an acute angle that opens clockwise.

   ∠ ABC measures 40°

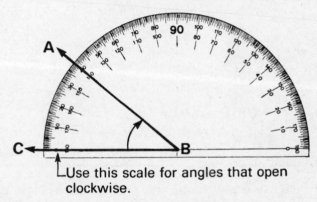

Use this scale for angles that open clockwise.

Measure each angle and circle the letter of the correct multiple-choice response.

5. ∠ ABC measures _____.

   The name given to ∠ ABC is _____.
   a) acute
   b) right
   c) obtuse
   d) straight
   e) reflex

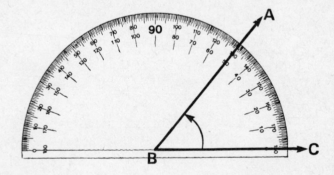

6. ∠ RST measures _____.

   The name given to ∠ RST is _____.
   a) acute
   b) right
   c) obtuse
   d) straight
   e) reflex

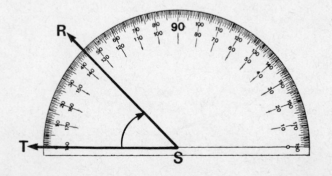

7. ∠ DEF measures _____.

The name given to ∠ DEF is _____.
a) acute
b) right
c) obtuse
d) straight
e) reflex

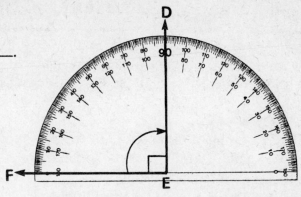

8. ∠ LMN measures _____.

The name given to ∠ LMN is _____.
a) acute
b) right
c) obtuse
d) straight
e) reflex

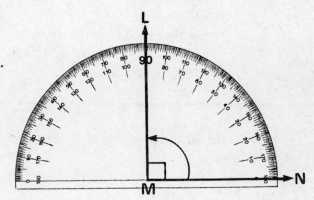

9. ∠ XYZ measures _____.

The name given to ∠ XYZ is _____.
a) acute
b) right
c) obtuse
d) straight
e) reflex

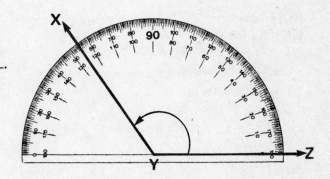

10. ∠ CDE measures _____.

The name given to ∠ CDE is _____.
a) acute
b) right
c) obtuse
d) straight
e) reflex

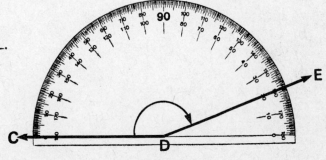

DRAWING AN ANGLE WITH A PROTRACTOR

To draw an angle with a protractor, draw one side along the 0° line. Draw the other side crossing the protractor scale at the desired degree mark.

EXAMPLE: Using a protractor, draw a 20° angle that opens counterclockwise ⟩ .

Step 1. Draw one side of the angle along the 0° line to the right of the center mark of the protractor.

Step 2. Draw the second side to cross the protractor scale at 20° on the counterclockwise scale, the inner scale.

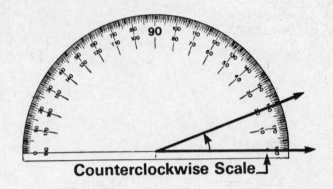

Counterclockwise Scale

Draw each angle on the protractor to the right and answer each question as indicated.

1. Draw an angle of 75° that opens counterclockwise ⟩ .

   If the sides of a 75° angle are doubled in length, the size of the angle _____ .

   a) doubles to 150°
   b) is halved to 37½°
   c) stays the same
   d) is increased to 300°
   e) none of the above

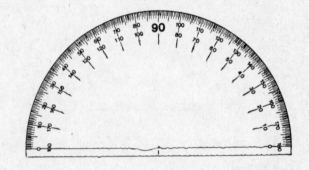

2. Draw a 162° angle that opens clockwise ⟨ .

   A 162° angle is _____ than a straight angle.

   a) 62° smaller
   b) 18° smaller
   c) 90° larger
   d) 28° larger
   e) none of the above

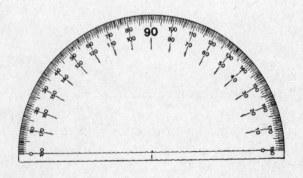

3. Draw an angle of 40° that opens
clockwise ⌒ .

    A 40° angle is equal to _____ of a
complete circle.

a) $\frac{1}{2}$

b) $\frac{1}{6}$

c) $\frac{1}{9}$

d) $\frac{1}{3}$

e) $\frac{1}{10}$

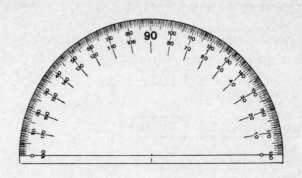

4. Draw a 125° angle that opens
counterclockwise ⌒ .

    An angle measuring 125° is _____
than a right angle.

a) 35° smaller

b) 25° larger

c) 55° larger

d) 35° larger

e) 25° smaller

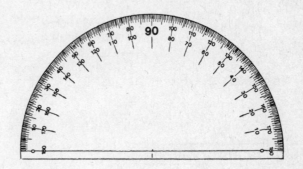

5. Draw a right angle that opens
counterclockwise ⌒ .

    An angle that is half the size of a
right angle measures _____.

a) 90°

b) 30°

c) 45°

d) 180°

e) 145°

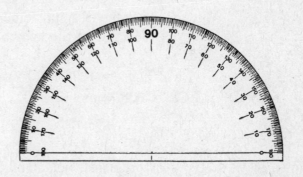

PAIRS OF ANGLES

As you've seen, a special name is given to an angle according to its size. Also, names are given to special pairs of angles. The names and relationships you should become familiar with are *complementary angles*, *supplementary angles*, and *vertical angles*.

Complementary Angles

Complementary angles are angles whose sum is 90°.

In the drawing at the right, line TR divides the right angle QRS into the two complementary angles, ∠ QRT and ∠ TRS.

∠ QRT is called the *complement* of ∠ TRS.

Often, the value of one complementary angle is given, and you are asked to find the value of the other.

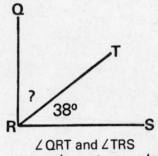

∠ QRT and ∠ TRS
are *complementary angles*:
∠ QRT + ∠ TRS = 90°

EXAMPLE: Find ∠ QRT if ∠ TRS = 38°.

To find the value of a complementary angle, subtract the known angle from 90°.

∠ QRT = 90°−38° = **52°**

Answer: ∠ QRT = **52°**.

Supplementary Angles

Supplementary angles are angles whose sum is 180°.

In the drawing at right, line RC divides the straight angle BCD into the two supplementary angles ∠ BCR and ∠ RCD.

∠ BCR is called the *supplement* of ∠ RCD.

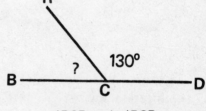

∠ BCR and ∠ RCD
are *supplementary angles*:
∠ BCR + ∠ RCD = 180°

EXAMPLE: Find ∠ *BCR* if ∠ RCD = 130°

To find the value of a supplementary angle, subtract the value of the known angle from 180°.

∠ BCR = 180°−130° = **50°**

Answer: ∠ BCR = **50°**.

Note: In these types of problems, you may be given an angle and be asked to find its *complement* or *supplement*.

Vertical Angles

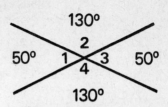

Vertical angles are formed when two straight lines cross at a point.

Vertical angles lie across from each other and are equal. In the drawing at right, ∠1 and ∠3 are vertical angles, and ∠2 and ∠4 are vertical angles.

Vertical angles are equal:
∠1 = ∠3 and ∠2 = ∠4

EXAMPLE: If ∠1 = 50°, then ∠3 = 50°, and if
∠2 = 130°, then ∠4 = 130°

Note: When two lines cross, each acute angle is supplementary to each obtuse angle. For example, ∠1 + ∠2 = 180°.

Find the value of each angle indicated below.

1. ∠ABD = _____

2. ∠TRS = _____

3. ∠XYO = _____

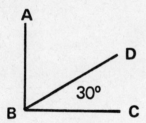

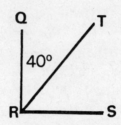

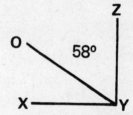

4. ∠MNP = _____

5. ∠DBC = _____

6. ∠OPT = _____

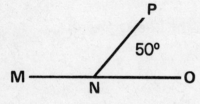

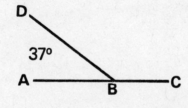

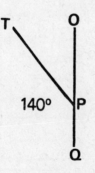

7. ∠b = _____
   ∠c = _____
   ∠d = _____

8. ∠1 = _____
   ∠3 = _____
   ∠4 = _____

9. ∠a = _____
   ∠b = _____
   ∠c = _____

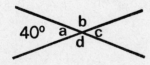

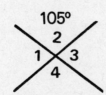

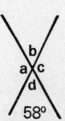

PAIRS OF ANGLES: APPLYING YOUR SKILLS

Practical problems involving pairs of angles often require you to find an unknown angle. A few common examples that frequently appear include:

- finding an angle between a ladder and the ground
- finding an angle between two boards or beams
- finding an angle between intersecting streets
- finding a missing "corner of the room" angle

In each case, you are really being asked to find the complement or supplement of a given angle or to recognize an equal vertical angle. You'll have a chance to practice each of the above examples in this section.

In books and on tests, practical problems often appear as word problems. You may or may not be given an accompanying drawing. In either case, the first step in solving a word problem is to represent the information in the problem by a drawing that contains only straight lines. Then, solve the straight-line drawing by using the skills you learned on the previous few pages.

EXAMPLE: A ladder leans against the side of a house. The ladder makes an acute angle of 61° with the ground. What is the value of the obtuse angle the ladder makes with the ground?

In this word problem, no drawing is given.

For comparison, look at both an accurate picture and a straight-line drawing.

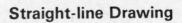

Straight-line Drawing

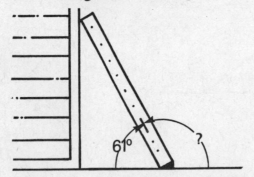

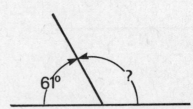

Notice that the use of a straight-line drawing simplifies the problem by focusing attention on the unknown angle. You can see that the question in the problem really asks,

"What is the supplement of 61°?"

Find the supplement of 61° by subtracting 61° from 180°.

Supplement of 61° = 180° − 61° = **119°**

Answer: The obtuse angle is 119°.

For each drawing below, solve for the unmeasured angle as indicated.

1. The diagonal bridge support piece makes an angle of 50° with the cross beam. What angle does it make with the upright beam?

    _____

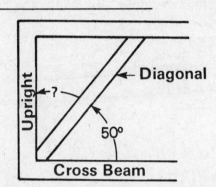

2. Ohio Street intersects Seventh Avenue as shown below. What are the values of the three unmeasured angles?

    ∠1 = _____

    ∠2 = _____

    ∠3 = _____

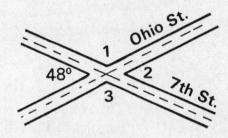

In problems 3 through 5, make a line drawing if you find it helpful.

3. A ladder is leaning against the side of a barn. If the ladder makes an acute angle of 82° with the ground, what is the size of the supplementary angle the ladder makes with the ground?

    _____

4. Four angles are formed when two straight lines cross. If one of the angles is 90°, what is the value of each of the other angles?

    _____ _____ _____

5. What is the supplement of 147°?

    _____

Refer to the drawing at the right, and match each *expression* with its equivalent *value*. Write the letter of the correct value before each expression. Although this may look difficult, you can find all of the answers by using what you have learned about the relationships between complementary, supplementary, and vertical angles.

	Expression	*Value*
_____	6. ∠1	a) 180°
_____	7. ∠4 + ∠5	b) 90°
_____	8. ∠5	c) 360°
_____	9. ∠1 + ∠2	d) 45°
_____	10. ∠1 + ∠2 + ∠3 + ∠4 + ∠5	e) 135°

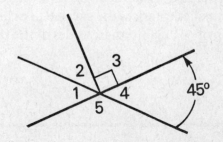

PARALLEL LINES CUT BY A TRANSVERSAL

Parallel lines are lines that run side-by-side and do not cross at any point. Lines A and B in the drawing below are parallel lines.

A *transversal* is a third line that crosses two parallel lines. The line labeled "*t*" in the drawing is a transversal.

When a transversal crosses two parallel lines, a set of four angles is formed at each point of intersection.

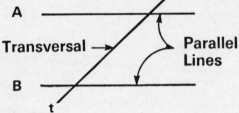

> **Note:** The symbol for "parallel" is "∥". To write "Line A is parallel to Line B" in symbols, write:
>
> A∥B

Since one set of angles looks exactly like the other set of angles, the following relations are true:

I. *Corresponding Angles Are Equal*
   If you cut the transversal in half and place one set of angles over the other, corresponding angles would sit on top of each other.

$$\angle 1 = \angle 5 \qquad \angle 3 = \angle 7$$
$$\text{and}$$
$$\angle 2 = \angle 6 \qquad \angle 4 = \angle 8$$

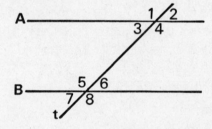

II. *Alternate Interior Angles Are Equal*
   Alternate interior angles are angles that are inside (interior) the parallel lines and that are on opposite (alternate) sides of the transversal.

$$\angle 3 = \angle 6$$
$$\angle 4 = \angle 5$$

III. *Alternate Exterior Angles Are Equal*
   Alternate exterior angles are angles that are outside (exterior) the parallel lines and that are on opposite (alternate) sides of the transversal.

$$\angle 1 = \angle 8$$
$$\angle 2 = \angle 7$$

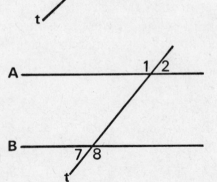

You will seldom need to remember the definitions introduced on the previous page. However, you should remember the angle relationships when two parallel lines are cut by a transversal. These relationships are most easily remembered as follows.

- The four acute angles are equal.
- The four obtuse angles are equal.
- Each acute angle is supplementary to each obtuse angle.

EXAMPLE: Parallel lines E and F are cut by transversal "r". The acute angle at the upper right is 50°. Label the other seven angles in the figure.

Step 1. Label the acute angle at the upper right as 50°.

Step 2. Label all other acute angles as 50°.

Step 3. The supplement of 50° is found by subtracting 50° from 180°.

$$180° - 50° = \mathbf{130°}$$

Label each obtuse angle as 130°.

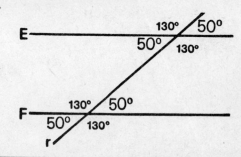

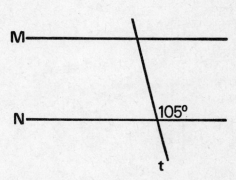

In the figures below, label each angle with its value.

1. A∥B

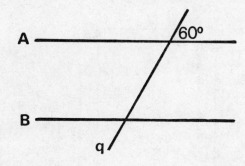

2. M∥N

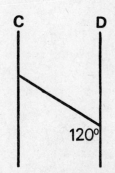

3. A∥B

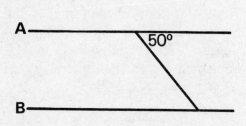

(*Hint:* Extend an imaginary transversal across each parallel line.)

4. C∥D

(*Hint:* Don't be fooled just because the figure is turned.)

PARALLEL LINES CUT BY A TRANSVERSAL: APPLYING YOUR SKILLS

In each drawing below, solve for the unmeasured angle as indicated.

1. Jackson Street crosses Twenty-third and Twenty-fourth Streets at an angle of 70°. What is the value of angle "c" in the drawing below?

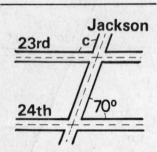

2. The diagonal brace in the fence gate makes an angle of 50° with the vertical side piece on the left. What angle does the brace make with the vertical side piece on the right?

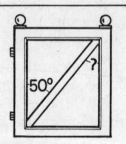

3. The commuter train crosses Monroe and Madison Avenues as shown below. What is the value of the angle labeled "a" in the drawing?

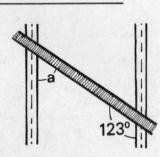

4. Lincoln Street joins Eighth and Ninth as shown below. How many degrees are in angle D, the obtuse angle that Lincoln makes with Ninth?

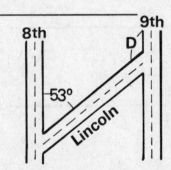

5. The side of the A-frame house below makes an angle of 130° with the ground. What is the value of the angle that the side makes with the rafter?

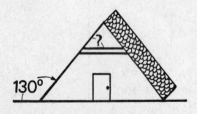

6. A parallelogram is a four-sided figure with two pairs of parallel lines. Using your knowledge of angles, find the sum of the four angles of a parallelogram. (*Hint*: Each obtuse angle is supplementary to each acute angle.)

$\angle A + \angle B + \angle C + \angle D =$ _____

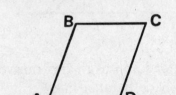

7. The Big H Clothing Company designed a new symbol to place on its products. The designer suggested that all acute angles should be 60°. What is the measure of each obtuse angle?

_____

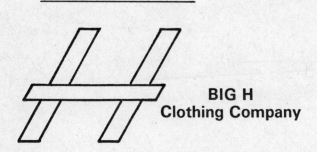

**BIG H
Clothing Company**

8. The capital letter "I" is an example of parallel lines joined by a transversal. Name four other capital letters that are similar examples.

_____

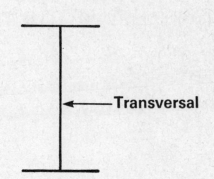

← **Transversal**

Parallel lines often occur in patterns. Don't let these patterns confuse you. Look for the parallel lines and transversals in the drawings below. Notice that you are asked to find an angle that is equal to or the supplement of a given angle.

9. In the drawing below showing two sets of three parallel lines, which angle ($\angle$ b or $\angle$ c) is equal to $\angle$ a?

_____

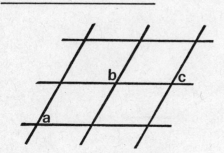

10. A crochet pattern on the edge of a baby blanket is designed as a "zigzag" between parallel lines. In the drawing below, what is the value of angle "w"? $\angle$ v = 60°

$\angle$ w = _____

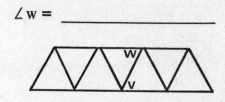

11. The shelf brace below makes an obtuse angle of 145° with the lower shelf. What acute angle does the brace make with the upper shelf?

_____

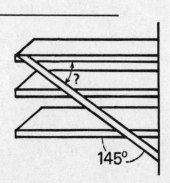

145°

12. Cross braces are often used in the framing of a house. In the drawing below, what is the value of the angle labeled "b"?

_____

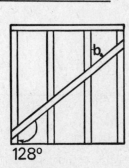

128°

FINAL ANGLES SKILLS INVENTORY

Problems 1-3: Write the symbol (letter name) that represents each angle below.

1. Symbol:_____

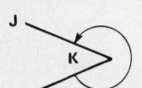

2. Symbol:_____

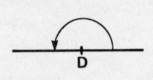

3. Symbol:_____

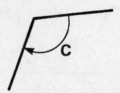

Problems 4 and 5: Circle the letter of the correct multiple-choice response.

4. Angle CDE is a(n) _____ angle.
   a) acute
   b) right
   c) obtuse
   d) straight
   e) reflex

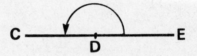

5. Angle XYZ is a(n) _____ angle.
   a) acute
   b) right
   c) obtuse
   d) straight
   e) reflex

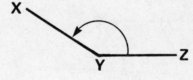

6. Measure ∠ FGH.

   ∠ FGH = _____

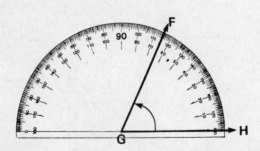

7. Measure ∠ QRS.

   ∠ QRS = _____

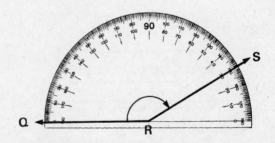

8. Use the protractor below and draw a 165° angle that opens counter-clockwise ⌒ .

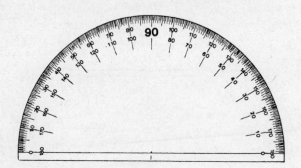

9. Use the protractor below and draw a 45° angle that opens clockwise ⌒ .

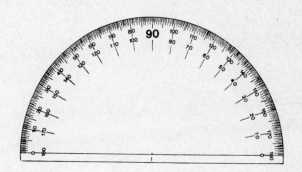

10. What is the value of ∠ CDE in the drawing below?

_____

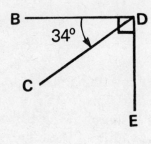

11. As shown in the drawing below, a mirror frame has a 60° angle in the corner. What is the size of the complementary angle marked "a" in the drawing?

_____

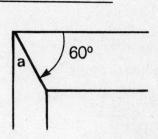

12. What is the complement of 71°?

_____

13. A door, placed next to a corner of a room, is open at an 80° angle, almost touching a wall. What is the value of the complementary angle that the door makes with the wall?

_____

14. What is the value of ∠ TUV in the drawing below?

_____

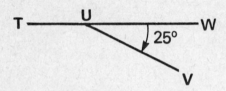

15. The shelf support, drawn below, forms a 40° acute angle with the wall. How large is the obtuse angle that the support forms with the wall?

_____

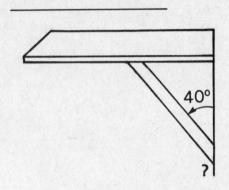

16. What is the supplement of 143°?

_____

17. Webster Street intersects Thirty-fourth Avenue at a 65° acute angle. What is the value of the supplementary angle that Webster makes with Thirty-fourth?

_____

18. What are the values of ∠ a, ∠ b, and ∠ c in the drawing below?

∠ a = _____

∠ b = _____

∠ c = _____

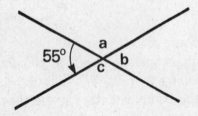

19. The two walking paths in Central Park cross near the fountain as shown in the drawing below. What are the values of the other three angles at this intersection?

∠ 1 = _____

∠ 2 = _____

∠ 3 = _____

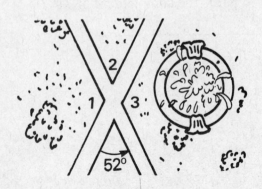

20. In the figure below, label each angle with its value.

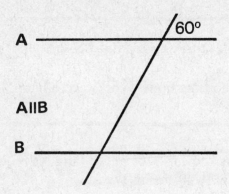

21. Front Street intersects Fifty-first at an angle of 62° as shown. Label each angle at both intersections with its value.

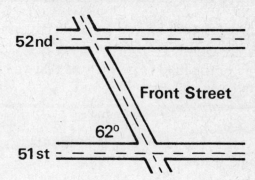

FINAL ANGLES INVENTORY CHART

Circle the number of any problem that you missed and be sure to review the appropriate page. A passing score is 18 correct answers. If you miss more than three questions, you should review this chapter.

Problem	Skill Area	Page
1	labeling angles	12
2	labeling angles	12
3	labeling angles	12
4	types of angles	10
5	types of angles	10
6	measuring angles	13+14
7	measuring angles	13+14
8	drawing angles	16
9	drawing angles	16
10	pairs of angles	18+19
11	pairs of angles: applying skills	20
12	pairs of angles	18+19
13	pairs of angles: applying skills	20
14	pairs of angles	18+19
15	pairs of angles: applying skills	20
16	pairs of angles	18+19
17	pairs of angles: applying skills	20
18	pairs of angles	18+19
19	pairs of angles: applying skills	20
20	parallel lines cut by transversal	22+23
21	parallel lines: applying skills	24

TRIANGLES

TRIANGLES SKILLS INVENTORY

This inventory will let you know what you need to work on in the TRIANGLES section of *Number Power: Geometry*.

Do all of the following problems that you can. There is no time limit. Work carefully and check all your answers.

---

1. What is the value of ∠B in the triangle below?

_____

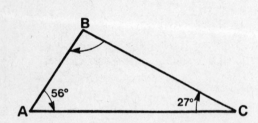

2. What is the top roof angle (angle a) in the drawing below?

_____

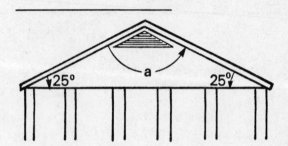

3. The sum of two angles in a triangle is 117°. What is the value of the third angle?

_____

Problems 4 and 5: Circle the letter of the correct multiple-choice response.

4. The name given to triangle DEF is

_____.

  a) equilateral
  b) isosceles
  c) right
  d) scalene
  e) "b" and "d"

5. The name given to triangle QRS is

_____.

  a) equilateral
  b) isosceles
  c) right
  d) scalene
  e) "c" and "d" above

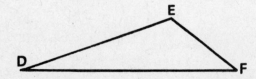

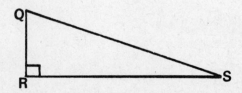

6. Find x: $\frac{x}{12} = \frac{2}{3}$

_____

7. Triangles ABC and XYZ are similar triangles. What is the length of side YZ in triangle XYZ?

_____

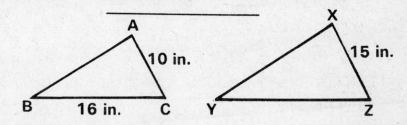

8. In triangle OPQ, $\angle$ O = 42° and $\angle$ P = 31°. In triangle XYZ, $\angle$ X = 31° and $\angle$ Y = 107°. Is triangle OPQ similar to triangle XYZ?

_____

9. To find the distance (d) across Boot Lake, Jane measured the distances as shown on her drawing. Noting that the two triangles are similar, find the distance for "d". (Distances are measured in yards.)

_____

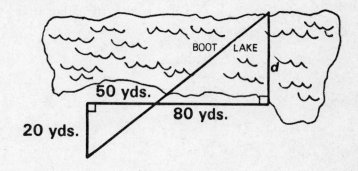

10. To find the height of a fir tree, Bill first found the length of the tree's shadow to be 80 feet long. At the same time, he held a yardstick perpendicular to the ground. The yardstick cast a shadow of 4 feet. What was the height of the tree? (_Hint_: How many feet are in a yardstick?)

_____

11. Find the square of each number as indicated below.

a) $3^2 =$ _____   c) $7^2 =$ _____

b) $5^2 =$ _____   d) $9^2 =$ _____

12. Find each square root as indicated below.

a) $\sqrt{4}$ = _____   c) $\sqrt{64}$ = _____

b) $\sqrt{36}$ = _____   d) $\sqrt{100}$ = _____

13. What is the length of the hypotenuse of the triangle to the right?

_____

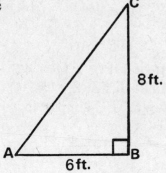

14. As shown in the drawing, the support piece for the billboard attaches to the billboard 12 feet above the ground. The support piece attaches to the ground 5 feet from the base of the billboard. What is the length of the support piece?

_____

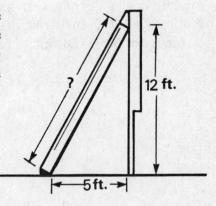

15. One side of a right triangle measures 15 feet. The hypotenuse measures 17 feet. What is the length of the third side?

_____

TRIANGLES INVENTORY CHART

Use this inventory to see what you already know about triangles and what you need to work on. A passing score is 12 correct answers. Even if you have a passing score, circle the number of any problem that you miss, correct it, and turn to the practice page indicated.

Problem	Skill Area	Page
1	sum of angles	36
2	sum of angles: applying skills	38
3	sum of angles	36
4	definitions of triangles	40
5	definitions of triangles	40
6	similar triangles: proportion	46
7	similar triangles	48
8	similar triangles	44
9	similar triangles: applying skills	52
10	similar triangles: applying skills	52
11	squares	54
12	square roots	55
13	Pythagorean Theorem	56
14	Pythagorean Theorem: applying skills	60
15	Pythagorean Theorem	58

INTRODUCING TRIANGLES

A triangle is a plane (flat) figure that has three sides and three angles. Triangles appear in a variety of shapes and sizes.

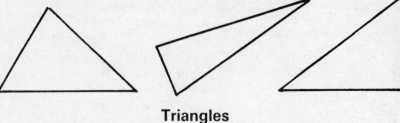

Triangles

Labeling A Triangle

The most common way to label a triangle is with three letters; one letter is placed at the vertex of each angle.

The symbol for "triangle" is "△"— a small triangle with three equal sides.

EXAMPLE: The triangle at the right is represented in symbols as "△ABC".

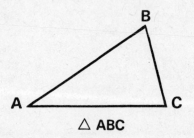

△ ABC

Note: The three vertex letters are usually written in alphabetical order.

Representing A Side Of A Triangle

The side of a triangle is represented by the two letters at the two ends of that side.

EXAMPLE: Side ST is the side *opposite* (across from) ∠R.
In △ RST, side RS is the longest side.

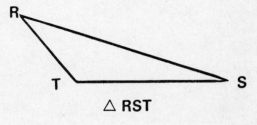

△ RST

Note: The longest side of a triangle is always opposite the largest angle.

Representing An Angle In A Triangle

An angle in a triangle is most often represented by the angle's vertex letter only.

EXAMPLE: In △DEF, the 30° angle is labeled D and usually identified as ∠D.

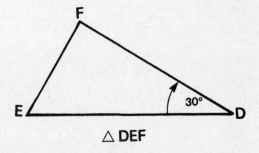

△ DEF

Note: As you saw in the last chapter, ∠D can also be called ∠EDF or ∠FDE. When an angle is represented by all three letters, the angle's vertex letter is written second.

Write the symbol (in alphabetical order) that represents each figure below.

1. _____

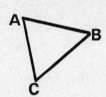

2. _____

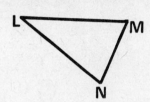

3. _____

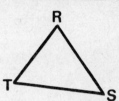

Name the side that is opposite the measured angle in each triangle below.

4. _____

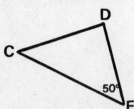

5. _____

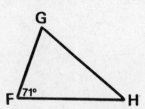

6. _____

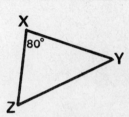

Using a single letter only, name the angle that is opposite a measured side in each triangle below.

7. _____

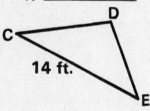

8. _____

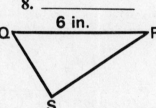

9. _____

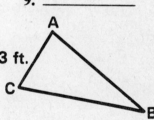

Referring to the triangle below, complete each sentence.

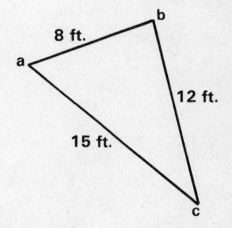

10. The angle opposite the side that has a length of 8 feet is labeled _____.

11. The length of the side opposite ∠a is _____.

12. The angle opposite the side that has a length of 15 feet is labeled _____.

13. The length of the side opposite ∠c is _____.

14. The angle opposite the side that has a length of 12 feet is labeled _____.

15. The largest angle shown is _____.

THE SUM OF ANGLES IN A TRIANGLE

One of the most important rules to learn in the study of geometry is the following:

Rule: The sum of the three angles in a triangle is equal to 180°.

Referring to the triangle at the right, you can write this rule in symbols:

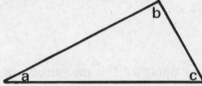

$$\angle a + \angle b + \angle c = 180°$$

To see why this rule is true, enclose a triangle in parallel lines and use information that you learned in the chapter on angles.

You know that $\angle d + \angle b + \angle e = 180°$ since together they make up a straight angle.

Also, you know that $\angle a = \angle d$ and $\angle c = \angle e$ since these are pairs of opposite interior angles.

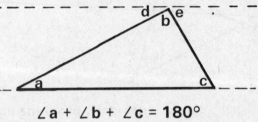

$$\angle a + \angle b + \angle c = \textbf{180°}$$

Thus, the sum $\angle a + \angle b + \angle c$ is equal to $\angle d + \angle b + \angle e$, which is 180°.

The rule stated above is commonly used to find the third angle in a triangle when the other two are known. To find the third angle, subtract the sum of the two known angles from 180°.

EXAMPLE 1:   What is the value of $\angle B$ in triangle ABC?
   Step 1.   Add $\angle A$ and $\angle C$.
       $\angle A + \angle C = 32° + 47° = 79°$
   Step 2.   To find $\angle B$, subtract 79° from 180°.
       $\angle B = 180° - 79° = \textbf{101°}$
   Answer: $\angle B = \textbf{101°}$

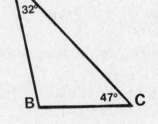

EXAMPLE 2:   What is the value of $\angle D$ in the right
       triangle DEF?
   Step 1.   Add $\angle E$ and $\angle F$. Remember: $\angle E = 90°$.
       $\angle E + \angle F = 90° + 36° = 126°$
   Step 2.   To find $\angle D$, subtract 126° from 180°.
       $\angle D = 180° - 126° = \textbf{54°}$
   Answer: $\angle D = \textbf{54°}$

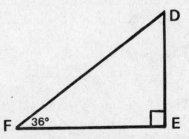

Find the value of the unmeasured angle in each triangle below.

1. _____

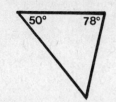

2. _____

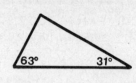

3. _____

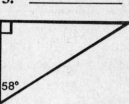

4. _____

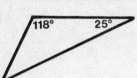

5. _____

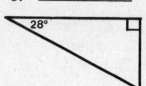

6. _____

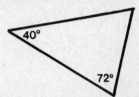

7. _____

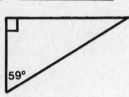

8. _____

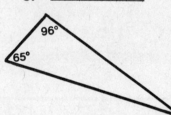

9. _____

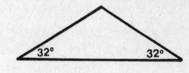

10. In triangle RST, $\angle R = 45°$ and $\angle S = 52°$. What is the value of $\angle T$?

_____

11. Angle C in triangle ABC is a right angle. If angle B is equal to 35°, what is the value of angle A?

_____

12. In $\triangle$ XYZ, each of two angles is equal to 38°. What is the value of the third angle?

_____

THE SUM OF ANGLES IN A TRIANGLE: APPLYING YOUR SKILLS

Knowing that a triangle contains 180° is useful in finding the third angle of a triangle when the first two are known.

EXAMPLE: The support cable for a telephone pole makes an angle of 63° with the ground. What angle does the cable make with the pole?

Note: In problems like this, the telephone pole is assumed to make a 90° angle with the ground.

Step 1. Add 63° and 90°.

$$63° + 90° = 153°$$

Step 2. To find the unknown angle, subtract 153° from 180°.

$$180° - 153° = 27°$$

Answer: **The cable makes an angle of 27° with the pole.**

---

1. A shelf support makes an angle of 48° with the wall. What is the value of the angle the support makes with the shelf?

_____

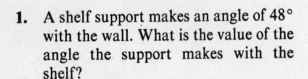

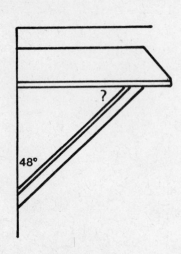

2. To properly cut her greenhouse roof side piece, what is the third angle Joyce needs to know?

_____

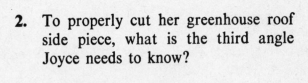

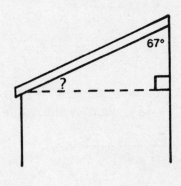

3. Carey leaned a ladder against the house. If the ladder makes an angle of 62° with the ground, what angle does it make with the house?

_____

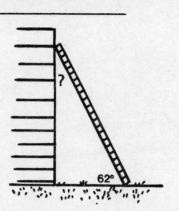

4. What is the value of the unmeasured roof angle in the drawing below?

_____

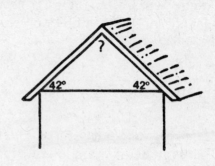

5. The walking paths in City Park meet in a triangle around the rose garden. What is the value of the unmeasured angle in this triangle?

_____

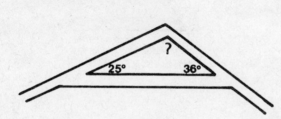

6. A dress design calls for a triangular piece of material. If one angle is a right angle and a second angle is 35°, what is the value of the third angle?

_____

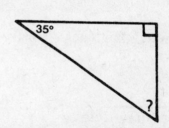

7. A quilt pattern requires pieces of colored cloth cut in the shape of a triangle. Each triangle is to have three equal angles and three equal sides. What is the value of each of the three equal angles in a triangle?

_____

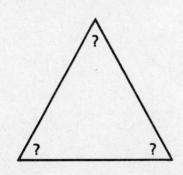

8. A surveyor drove a stick into the ground. He then dropped a line from the top of the stick and anchored it into the ground in front of the stick. If the angles shown below are correct, does the stick make a 90° angle with the ground?

_____

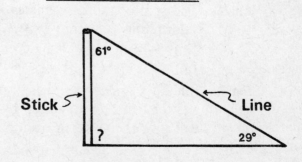

WORKING WITH DEFINITIONS OF TRIANGLES

There are three types of triangles: equilateral, isosceles, and scalene. Knowing the characteristics of these types of triangles is necessary in solving many types of problems. In this section, definitions and examples of problems you should be familiar with are given.

Equilateral Triangle

An *equilateral triangle* has three equal angles. Each angle measures 60°. Also, all three sides of an equilateral triangle are equal.

An equilateral triangle is also called an *equiangular triangle*.

EXAMPLE: What is the value of each angle in the triangle at the right?

Since all three sides are equal, the triangle is equilateral. Thus, all three angles are equal, and each angle is equal to 60°.

$$180° \div 3 = 60°$$

Answer: Each angle equals 60°.

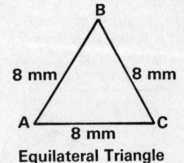

Equilateral Triangle

Isosceles Triangle

An *isosceles triangle* has two equal angles. The sides opposite the equal angles are also equal.

The two equal angles are called *base angles*. The third angle is called the *vertex angle*.

EXAMPLE 1:   What is the value of each base angle in the isosceles triangle at the right?

Step 1.   The sum of the base angles is found by subtracting 50° from 180°.

$$180° - \angle y = \angle x + \angle z$$
$$180° - 50° = 130° \ (\angle x + \angle z)$$

Step 2.   Since $\angle x$ and $\angle z$ are equal, divide your answer from the first step by 2. This will give the value of each base angle.

$$130° \div 2 = 65°$$

Answer: Each base angle is 65°.

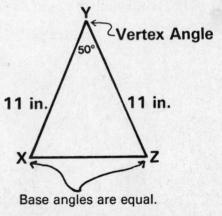

Base angles are equal.

Isosceles Triangle

EXAMPLE 2: What is the value of each of the two unmeasured angles in the isosceles triangle at the right?

Step 1. Since this triangle has two equal sides, it must have two equal angles. Thus, the base angles $\angle Q$ and $\angle S$ are equal.

$$\angle S = \angle Q = 70°$$

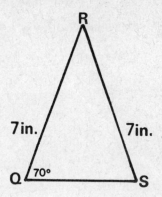

Step 2. $\angle R$, the vertex angle, is found by subtracting the sum of the base angles from 180°.

$$\angle Q + \angle S = 70° + 70° = 140°$$
$$\angle R = 180° - 140° = 40°$$

Answer: $\angle S = 70°$ and $\angle R = 40°$.

Scalene Triangle

A *scalene triangle* has no equal sides and no equal angles. The scalene triangle is the most common type of triangle.

To find a missing angle in a scalene triangle, subtract the two known angles from 180°.

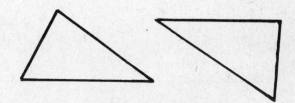

Scalene Triangles

Note: A triangle that has a right angle is often called a *right triangle*. Either an isosceles triangle or a scalene triangle can be a right triangle.

In an isosceles right triangle, one angle is 90°, and the other two angles are equal.

In a scalene right triangle, one angle is 90°, and the other two angles are not equal.

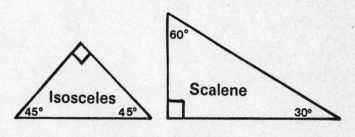

Right Triangles

EXAMPLE: What is the value of each base angle in the isosceles right triangle BCD?

Step 1. The sum of base angles is found by subtracting 90° ($\angle B$) from 180°.

$$180° - \angle B = \angle C + \angle D$$
$$180° - 90° = 90°$$

Step 2. To find $\angle C$ (and $\angle D$), divide 90° by 2.

$$\angle C = \angle D = \frac{90°}{2} = 45°$$

Answer: $\angle C = \angle D = 45°$.

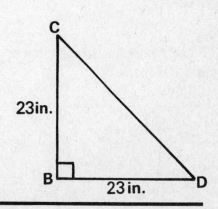

In each triangle below: a) Write the correct value for each unmeasured angle.
b) Name each triangle as equilateral, isosceles, or scalene.
c) Circle any triangle that is also a right triangle.

EXAMPLE: Problem   Answer
                                              Isosceles

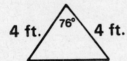

1. _____

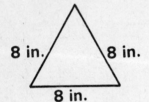

2. _____

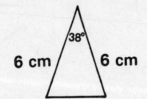

3. _____

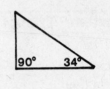

4. _____

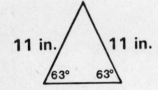

5. _____

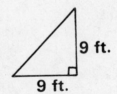

6. _____

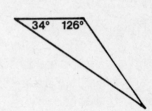

7. _____

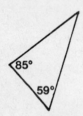

8. _____

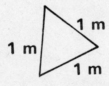

9. _____

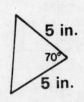

In each isosceles triangle below, determine the length of the side that is now labeled with a question mark (?).

10. _____

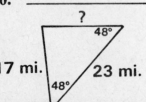

11. _____

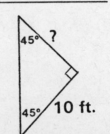

12. _____

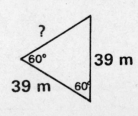

WORKING WITH DEFINITIONS OF TRIANGLES: APPLYING YOUR SKILLS

As a first step in solving each word problem below, draw the triangle that is described and label any angle whose value is given.

1. The vertex angle of an isosceles triangle is 80°. What is the value of each base angle?

   _____

2. In a scalene right triangle, one angle is equal to 35°. How large is the second acute angle?

   _____

3. Two of the angles in a scalene triangle measure 28° and 57°. What does the third angle measure?

   _____

4. If the three sides of triangle XYZ are equal, what is the value of each angle?

   _____

5. If a triangular figure is in the shape of an isosceles right triangle, what is the value of each base angle?

   _____

6. A billiards ball rack is shaped like a triangle with three equal sides. At what acute angle does each pair of sides meet?

   _____

7. A child's toy block is in the shape of a triangle. One angle measures 32° and another angle measures 17°. What is the value of the third angle?

   _____

8. The roof gable on Charlene's house has two equal sides. One angle measures 112°. The other two angles are equal to each other. What does each of those two angles measure?

   _____

SIMILAR TRIANGLES

Triangles that have the same three angles are called _similar_ triangles. Similar triangles have the same shape and differ only in the length of their sides. The symbol "~" stands for "is similar to."

EXAMPLE 1: Triangle ABC is similar to triangle DEF.
　　　　　In symbols, we write △ ABC ~ △ DEF.

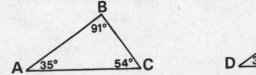

Equal angles in similar triangles are called _corresponding angles_. In △ ABC and △ DEF, each pair of corresponding angles is easily identified:

Corresponding Angles
Each triangle has a 35° angle: ∠ A = ∠ D.
Each triangle has a 91° angle: ∠ B = ∠ E.
Each triangle has a 54° angle: ∠ C = ∠ F.

Sides opposite corresponding angles are called _corresponding sides_. In △ ABC and △ DEF, each pair of corresponding sides are opposite equal angles:

Corresponding Sides
Sides opposite the 35° angles: sides BC and EF
Sides opposite the 91° angles: sides AC and DF
Sides opposite the 54° angles: sides AB and DE

EXAMPLE 2: In △ XYZ, ∠ X = 19° and ∠ Y = 76°.
　　　　　In △ HIJ, ∠ H = 85° and ∠ I = 19°.　Is △ XYZ similar to △ HIJ?

<u>Remember:</u> Triangles are similar if all three angles of one triangle are equal to all three angles of the second triangle.

Step 1. To find the third angle in △ XYZ, subtract the two known angles from 180°.

$$∠ X + ∠ Y = 19° + 76° = 95°$$
$$∠ Z = 180° - 95° = 85°$$

Step 2. To find the third angle in △ HIJ, subtract the two known angles from 180°.

$$∠ H + ∠ I = 85° + 19° = 104°$$
$$∠ J = 180° - 104° = 76°$$

Step 3. Compare the angles of the two triangles.

In △ XYZ, ∠ X = 19°, ∠ Y = 76°, and ∠ Z = 85°.
In △ HIJ, ∠ H = 85°, ∠ I = 19°, and ∠ J = 76°.

Answer: Yes. △ XYZ is similar to △ HIJ. Each triangle has the same three angles: 19°, 76°, and 85°.

Questions 1, 2, and 3 refer to triangles LMN and XYZ below.

△ LMN ~ △ XYZ

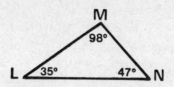 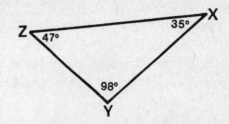

Answer the following questions:

1. Is △ LMN similar to △ XYZ? _____
    Why?_____

2. What are the three pairs of corresponding angles?
    a) ∠_____ = ∠_____   b) ∠_____ = ∠_____   c) ∠_____ = ∠_____

3. What are the three pairs of corresponding sides?
    a) _____ and _____   b) _____ and _____   c) _____ and _____

4. Of the following three triangles, which two are similar?
    _____ and _____

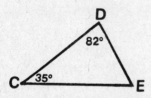 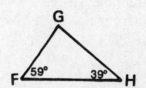 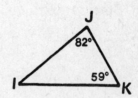

5. In △ LMN, ∠M = 24°, and ∠N = 107°.
    In △ PQR, ∠P = 107°, and ∠Q = 48°.
    Is △ LMN similar to △ PQR?

    _____

6. In △ ABC, ∠A = 50°, and ∠B = 42°.
    In △ DEF, ∠E = 88°, and ∠F = 50°.
    Is △ ABC similar to △ DEF?

    _____

Similar triangles are interesting because the lengths of corresponding sides are in *proportion* and can be written as *equivalent fractions*.

In your earlier work with mathematics, you worked with equivalent fractions; for instance $\frac{2}{4} = \frac{1}{2}$. A proportion is an example of equivalent fractions. In fact, the study of similar triangles is a use of equivalent fractions in geometry.

Example 3 below illustrates how to write corresponding sides as a proportion.

EXAMPLE 3: Because $\triangle ABC$ and $\triangle DEF$ have corresponding angles, they are similar triangles.

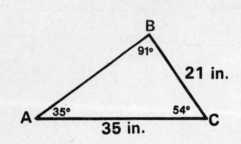
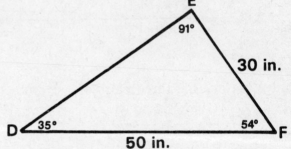

We can write a proportion as follows:

Step 1. Identify the pairs of corresponding sides.

　　a) AC and DF are corresponding sides.

　　b) BC and EF are corresponding sides.

Step 2. Write equivalent fractions (to be called a proportion from now on).

$$\frac{AC}{DF} = \frac{BC}{EF}$$

$$\frac{35}{50} = \frac{21}{30}$$

(To see that both sides of the proportion are equal, see that both can be reduced to $\frac{7}{10}$.)

In Example 3, it would have also been correct to write the proportion in this manner:

$$\frac{DF}{AC} = \frac{EF}{BC}$$

$$\frac{50}{35} = \frac{30}{21}$$

In both cases, the corresponding sides are on the same side of the equal sign.

To write the terms of the proportion in correct order, remember:
  (1) Each equivalent fraction consists of corresponding sides.
  (2) The numerator of each fraction is from one triangle.
  (3) The denominator of each fraction is from the other triangle.

___

For each pair of similar triangles below, fill in the missing term for each proportion. The first problem is done as an example.

1. <u>Problem</u>   <u>Answer</u>
$\frac{12}{36} = \frac{}{27}$ $\frac{12}{36} = \frac{9}{27}$

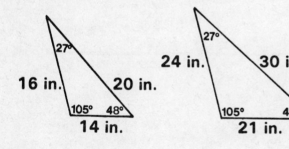

2. $\frac{7}{35} = \frac{}{20}$

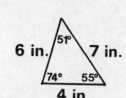 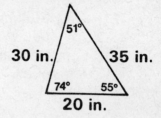

3. $\frac{}{30} = \frac{14}{21}$

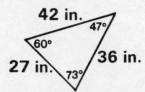

4. $\frac{15}{12} = \frac{10}{}$

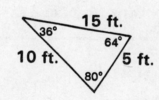 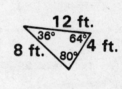

In problems 5 and 6, don't be fooled because the triangles are turned. Carefully find corresponding sides before completing each proportion.

5. $\frac{18}{} = \frac{15}{20}$

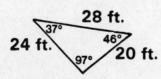

6. $\frac{40}{32} = \frac{}{24}$

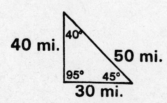 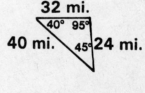

Example 4 shows how similar triangles can be used to find an unknown distance.

EXAMPLE 4: What is the length ℓ of the side LN in
△ LMN below?

    Step 1. Write a proportion using the correspond-
ing sides of triangles RST and LMN.

$$\frac{12}{9} = \frac{8}{\ell}$$

    Step 2. Solve the proportion by *cross-multiplying*.

To cross-multiply, follow steps a) and b):

a) Multiply the numerator of each fraction by the denominator of the other
fraction. Set the answers equal to each
other.

$$\frac{12}{9} \diagdown\!\!\!\!\diagup \frac{8}{\ell}$$

$$12\ell = 72$$

b) Divide the number standing alone by
the number next to the ℓ. Since 12
times ℓ equals 72, find ℓ by dividing 72
by 12.

$$\ell = \frac{72}{12} = 6$$

    Answer: Side LN has a length of 6 ft.

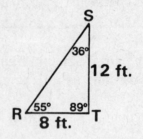

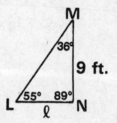

Find each length as indicated below.

1. △ ABC ～ △ RST. What is length
    "*d*"?

2. △ DEF ～ △ JKL. What is length
    "*x*"?

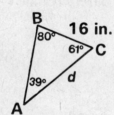

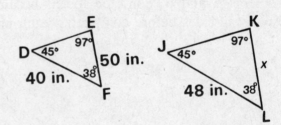

In problems 3 through 8, find corresponding sides before completing each proportion.

3. △ ABC ~ △ XYZ. What is length "*l*"?

_____

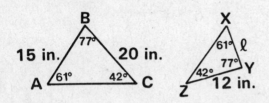

4. △ GHI ~ △ DEF. What is length "*d*"?

_____

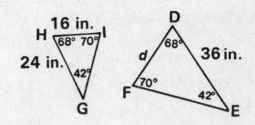

5. △ PQR ~ △ EFG. What is length "*b*"?

_____

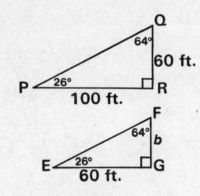

6. △ LMN ~ △ PQR. What is length "*x*"?

_____

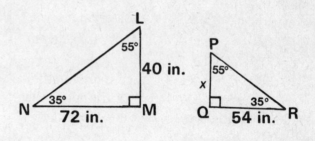

7. △ ABC ~ △ DEF. What is length "*s*"?

_____

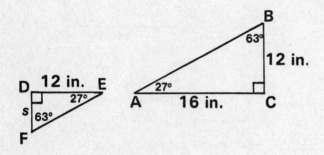

8. △XYZ ~ △ GHI. What is length "*l*"?

_____

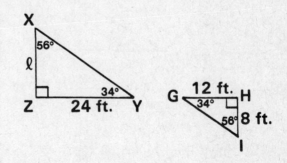

There are two geometric figures involving similar triangles that occur often in practical applications and on tests. Study the figures below in Examples 5 and 6 before working problems 1 through 4.

EXAMPLE 5: △ RST ~ △ RUV

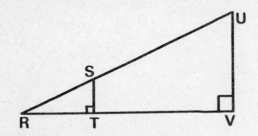

Do you see why △ RST is similar to △ RUV?

The reason is that each triangle has the same three angles:

a) ∠R is an angle in each triangle,

b) ∠RTS = ∠RVU; each is a right angle, and

c) ∠RST = ∠RUV. Since the two other angles are equal in both triangles, the third angle must also be the same.

Sample Question:

If ST = 10 ft., RT = 15 ft., and RV = 60 ft., what is the length of UV?

Solution:

Step 1. Many students find it helpful to draw the similar triangles separately as follows:

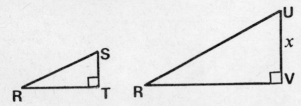

Step 2. Write a proportion. Let x stand for the unknown value of UV.

$$\frac{UV}{ST} = \frac{RV}{RT} \text{ or } \frac{x}{10} = \frac{60}{15}$$

Step 3. Solve the proportion for x.

$$15x = 600$$

$$x = \frac{600}{15} = 40$$

Therefore, UV = **40 ft.**

EXAMPLE 6: △ ABC ~ △ ADE

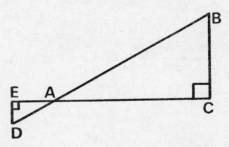

Do you see that △ ABC is similar to △ ADE?

a) ∠EAD = ∠BAC since they are vertical angles,

b) ∠AED = ∠ACB, since each is a right angle, and

c) ∠D = ∠B. Since the right angles and the vertical angles are equal, the remaining angles must be equal.

Sample Question:

If AC = 100 in., AE = 20 in., and DE = 15 in., what is the length of BC?

Solution:

Step 1. Again, you may find it helpful to draw the similar triangles separately:

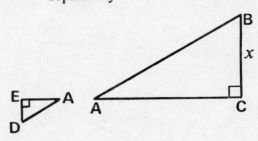

Step 2. Write a proportion.

$$\frac{AC}{AE} = \frac{BC}{DE} \text{ or } \frac{100}{20} = \frac{x}{15}$$

Step 3. Solve the proportion for x.

$$20x = 1500$$

$$x = \frac{1500}{20} = 75$$

Therefore, BC = **75 in.**

Find each length as indicated below.

1. EF = 10 cm, DF = 16 cm,
   DH = 48 cm
   What is the length of GH?

   _____

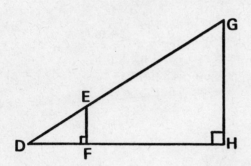

2. JF = 4 ft., FH = 12 ft.,
   JI = 3 ft.
   What is the length of GH?

   _____

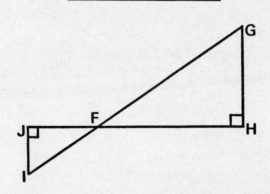

3. LM = 36 mi., MN = 80 mi.,
   PN = 20 mi.
   What is the length of OP?

   _____

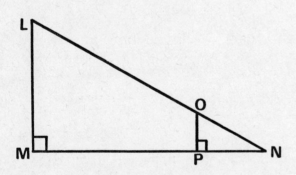

4. RS = 18 yds., ST = 6 yds.,
   TU = 4 yds.
   What is the length of QR?

   _____

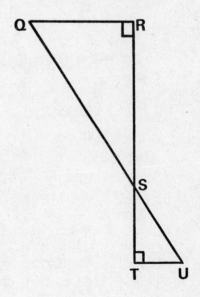

SIMILAR TRIANGLES: APPLYING YOUR SKILLS

Similar triangles are often used to solve practical problems that require you to find an unknown distance or height. You can imagine that the side of a triangle is formed by the height of an object, such as a building, tree, or person. Or, a side of a triangle may be formed by the distance across a river or a canyon. The pictures in the example below illustrate this.

To use similar triangles in a practical problem, follow these basic steps:

Identify the corresponding angles in the similar triangles.
Identify the corresponding sides—opposite the corresponding angles.
Write a proportion involving the unknown distance or height.
Solve the proportion by cross-multiplication.

EXAMPLE: Two trees stand side-by-side. The smaller tree is 18 feet high and casts a shadow of 30 feet. The larger tree casts a shadow of 55 feet. How high is the larger tree?

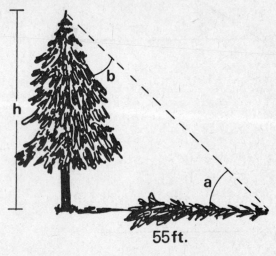

Note: To solve "shadow" problems, you should know that the sun's rays are parallel. This means that the sides opposite the right angles (the sides indicated by dotted lines in the drawing at right) form equal angles with the ground. In this example, this means that
$$\angle a = \angle c \text{ and } \angle b = \angle d.$$

Note: Each tree forms a right angle with the ground.

Step 1. Since $\angle a = \angle c$, the unknown height "h" and the height 18 feet are corresponding sides of similar triangles.

Also, the shadow lengths on the ground are corresponding sides. Knowing this, you can write the proportion:
$$\frac{h}{18} = \frac{55}{30}$$

Step 2. Solve the proportion by cross-multiplying and then dividing:
$$\frac{h}{18} \diagdown \frac{55}{30}$$
$$30h = 990$$
$$h = \frac{990}{30} = 33$$

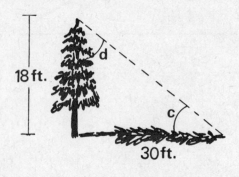

Answer: **The taller tree is 33 feet high.**

Solve each problem below for the unknown height or distance indicated.

1. A house stands next to a shed. The shed is 12 feet high and casts a shadow of 9 feet. At the same time, the house casts a shadow of 18 feet. How high is the top of the house?

_____

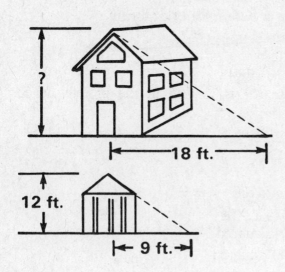

2. To measure the distance (*d*) across Green Lake, Bill marked off distances and drew the picture below. Use the similar triangles to solve for the distance across Green Lake.

_____

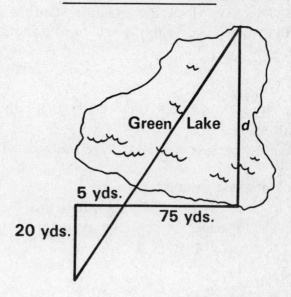

3. Joyce is standing next to a telephone pole. She walks along the shadow of the pole until the top of her shadow meets the top of the shadow of the pole. Joyce is 5 feet tall, and her shadow measures 8 feet. The shadow of the pole measures 112 feet. How tall is the pole?

_____

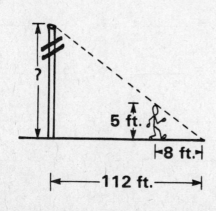

4. Laurie estimated the distance across Blue River by walking off distances and making the drawing below. Use her drawing to find the distance (*d*) across the river.

_____

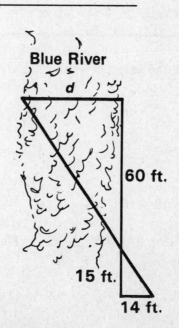

SQUARES AND SQUARE ROOTS

Before beginning the next topic, the *Pythagorean Theorem*, spend some time on these two pages strengthening your skills working with *squares* and *square roots*.

Squares

The *square* of a number is that number multiplied by itself.

For example, the square of 5 is $5 \times 5 = 25$.

In symbols, we write the square of a number as a *base and an exponent*.

5×5 is written 5^2 ⟵exponent, ⟵base

The *exponent* (2) tells how many times the *base* (5) is written in the product when multiplying.

We commonly read 5^2 as "five squared." The *value* of 5^2 is 25.

Look at these examples:

Product	As a base and an exponent	Read in words	Value
4×4	4^2	"4 squared"	16
11×11	11^2	"11 squared"	121
$b \times b$	b^2	"b squared"	*
$c \times c$	c^2	"c squared"	*

*A value for "letter squared" can only be found when we know the letter's value.

EXAMPLE: What is the value of "a^2" if $a = 7$?
Replace the letter "a" with the number 7.
$a^2 = 7^2 = 7 \times 7 = 49$

Answer: $a^2 = 49$ when $a = 7$

What is the value of each "squared" number or letter below?

1. $3^2 = $ _____

2. $8^2 = $ _____

3. $6^2 = $ _____

4. $9^2 = $ _____

5. $12^2 = $ _____

6. $10^2 = $ _____

7. $14^2 = $ _____

8. $15^2 = $ _____

9. a^2 for $a = 3$ _____

10. b^2 for $b = 7$ _____

11. c^2 for $c = 4$ _____

12. d^2 for $d = 17$ _____

13. x^2 for $x = 18$ _____

14. b^2 for $b = 13$ _____

Square Roots

The second skill to learn is finding a *square root*.

The square root of a number is found by asking, "What number times itself equals this?" For instance, what number times itself equals 4? The answer is <u>2</u> because $2 \times 2 = 4$. This is called finding the square root of 4 and can be written as $\sqrt{4}$.

The table below contains the squares of the numbers from 1 to 15. These squares are called *perfect squares* since their square roots are whole numbers. Familiarity with these will help you to work problems in the next section.

Table of Perfect Squares

$1^2 = 1$	$6^2 = 36$	$11^2 = 121$
$2^2 = 4$	$7^2 = 49$	$12^2 = 144$
$3^2 = 9$	$8^2 = 64$	$13^2 = 169$
$4^2 = 16$	$9^2 = 81$	$14^2 = 196$
$5^2 = 25$	$10^2 = 100$	$15^2 = 225$

The values on this table can be used to find either squares or square roots. For instance, look at $5^2 = 25$. This is also used to find that the $\sqrt{25} = 5$.

EXAMPLE: If $b^2 = 144$, what is the value of "b"?

Here the letter "b" stands for the square root of 144. In symbols, $b = \sqrt{144}$. To solve for "b," find 144 in the right column above and identify its square root.

Answer: b = 12

Use the Table of Perfect Squares to find each value below.

1. $7^2 = $ _____

2. $10^2 = $ _____

3. $3^2 = $ _____

4. $15^2 = $ _____

5. $8^2 = $ _____

6. $4^2 = $ _____

7. $b^2 = 121$
    $b = $ _____

8. $c^2 = 25$
    $c = $ _____

9. $x^2 = 144$
    $x = $ _____

10. $a^2 = 1$
     $a = $ _____

11. $d = \sqrt{81}$
     $d = $ _____

12. $c = \sqrt{4}$
     $c = $ _____

13. $x = \sqrt{169}$
     $x = $ _____

14. $a = \sqrt{36}$
     $a = $ _____

15. $b = \sqrt{196}$
     $b = $ _____

RIGHT TRIANGLES AND THE PYTHAGOREAN THEOREM

As you have seen, a right triangle has two sides that meet in a right angle. The side opposite the right angle is always called the *hypotenuse* and is the longest side of a right triangle.

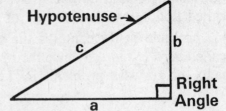

The Greek mathematician Pythagoras discovered an important relationship between the hypotenuse and the other two sides. He found that in a right triangle, the square of the hypotenuse is equal to the sum of the squares of the other two sides. We call this statement the *Pythagorean Theorem*.

In symbols, using the labels on the triangle above, we can write the Pythagorean Theorem as:
$$c^2 = a^2 + b^2$$

If you know the lengths of the other two sides, you can find the length of the hypotenuse by following these steps:

Step 1. Find the square of the other two sides (often called legs) separately.

Step 2. Add the squares of the sides found in Step 1.

Step 3. Solve for the hypotenuse by finding the square root of the sum of the squares found in Step 2.

EXAMPLE 1: What is the length of the hypotenuse of the triangle at right?

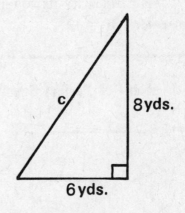

Step 1. Find the square of each side separately.

(a) Substitute 6 for "*a*" and find "a^2."
$$a^2 = 6^2 = 36$$

(b) Substitute 8 for "*b*" and find "b^2."
$$b^2 = 8^2 = 64$$

Step 2. Add the squares found in Step 1.
$$c^2 = a^2 + b^2 = 36 + 64 = 100$$

Step 3. Since $c^2 = a^2 + b^2$, set the sum of the squares found in Step 2 equal to c^2. Then to find c, take the square root of 100.
$$c^2 = 100$$
$$c = \sqrt{100} = \mathbf{10.}$$

Answer: **The length of the hypotenuse is 10 yards.**

Using the Pythagorean Theorem, find the length of each unmeasured side below. If you need to, refer to the Table of Perfect Squares on page 55.

1. _____

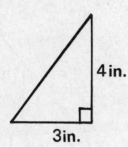

4 in.

3 in.

2. _____

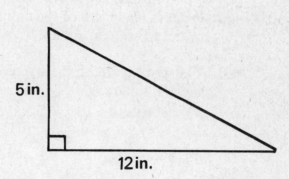

5 in.

12 in.

3. _____

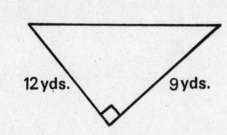

12 yds.   9 yds.

4. _____

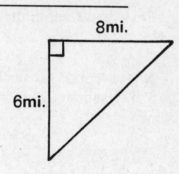

8 mi.

6 mi.

5. What is the length of the hypotenuse of a right triangle whose legs are 5 feet and 12 feet long?

    _____

6. Right triangle CDE has sides measuring 4 meters and 3 meters. The hypotenuse is longer than either of these two sides. What is the length of the hypotenuse?

    _____

The Pythagorean Theorem can also be used to find the length of a side if the lengths of the hypotenuse and one side are known.

EXAMPLE 2: What is the length of the unmeasured side of the triangle at right?

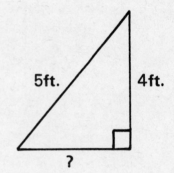

Step 1. Find the square of the hypotenuse. Next, find the square of the given side.
(a) Substitute 5 for *"c,"* and find *"c²."*
$$c^2 = 5^2 = 25$$
(b) Substitute 4 for *"b,"* and find *"b²."*
$$b^2 = 4^2 = 16$$

Note: You could substitute 4 for *"a"* instead of *"b."* A measured side can be called either *"a"* or *"b."*

Step 2. Write the Pythagorean Theorem:
$$c^2 = a^2 + b^2$$
From Step 1, substitute 25 for c^2 and 16 for b^2.
$$25 = a^2 + 16$$
Notice that 25 is equal to a^2 plus 16. To find a^2, subtract 16 from 25. This is written
$$a^2 = 25 - 16$$
$$a^2 = 9$$

Note: To see that you have solved for *"a²"* correctly, notice that $9 + 16 = 25$.

Step 3. Solve for "a" by taking the square root of 9.
$$a^2 = 9$$
$$\text{thus, } a = \sqrt{9} = 3$$

Answer: The length of the unmeasured side is 3 feet.

Using the Pythagorean Theorem, find the length of each unmeasured side below. If you need to, refer to the Table of Perfect Squares on page 55.

1. _____

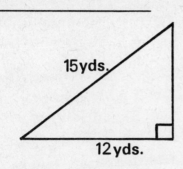

15yds.

12yds.

2. _____

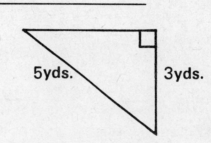

5yds.   3yds.

3. _____

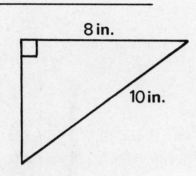

8 in.

10 in.

4. _____

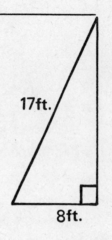

17ft.

8ft.

5. In right triangle ABC, the hypotenuse—side BC—is 13 inches long. Side AB is 5 inches long. What is the length of side AC?

_____

6. Triangle QRS is a right triangle. Side QR, the hypotenuse, has a length of 17 centimeters. Side RS has a length of 15 centimeters. What is the length of side QS?

_____

Note: Often, the sides of a right triangle have lengths of 3, 4, and 5 or a multiple of these, such as 6, 8, and 10. In these cases, the longest side, the hypotenuse, will be 5 or a multiple of 5. Problems 1, 2, and 3 illustrate this relationship.

RIGHT TRIANGLES AND THE PYTHAGOREAN THEOREM: APPLYING YOUR SKILLS

The Pythagorean Theorem is used to find the third side of a right triangle when the other two sides are known. In solving practical problems, be sure to correctly identify the hypotenuse as the side opposite the right angle.

Remember the Pythagorean Theorem: $c^2 = a^2 + b^2$, where c is the hypotenuse.

EXAMPLE: The support for a display sign attaches to the back of the sign 4 feet above the floor. The support rests on the floor 3 feet away. What is the length of the support?

Note: The support is the hypotenuse of a right triangle formed by the display sign and the floor.

Step 1.   Find the square of each side. Let $a = 3$ and $b = 4$.
$$a^2 = 3^2 = 9 \text{ and } b^2 = 4^2 = 16$$

Step 2.   To find c^2, add a^2 and b^2.
$$c^2 = a^2 + b^2$$
$$25 = 9 + 16$$
$$\text{thus, } c^2 = 25$$

Step 3.   Take the square root:
$$c = \sqrt{25} = 5$$

Answer: The length of the support is 5 feet.

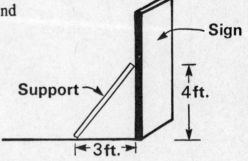

1. A mover's ramp is placed on top of a 5-foot-high staircase. If the end of the ramp is on the floor 12 feet away, how long is the ramp?

2. A telephone pole support cable attaches to the pole 20 feet high. If the cable is 25 feet long, how far from the bottom of the pole does the cable attach to the ground?

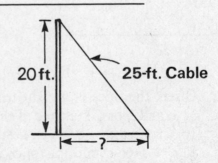

3. A _rectangle_ is a four-sided figure with four right angles. A _diagonal_ divides a rectangle into two right triangles. What is the length of the diagonal in the rectangle below?

_____

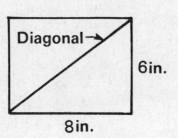

4. George leaned a 17-foot ladder against the house. The bottom of the ladder was 8 feet from the house. How high was the top of the ladder?

_____

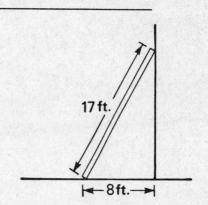

5. Joyce made a flower display in the front of her store. The display was in the shape of a right triangle. One side measured 5 feet, and the second side measured 12 feet. How long was the side opposite the right angle?

_____

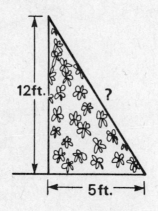

6. Mary is flying a model airplane at the end of a control line. The line is 17 yards long, and the plane is above a point on the ground that is 15 yards away from Mary. If the controls are held at a height of 1½ yards, how high is the plane off the ground?
(_Hint_: height = d + 1½)

_____

FINAL TRIANGLES SKILLS INVENTORY

1. What is the value of ∠R in the triangle below?

_____

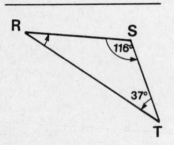

2. What is the missing angle Bill needs to find to cut his patio roof side piece?

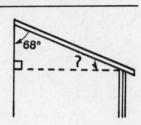

3. The sum of two angles in a triangle is 138°. What is the value of the third angle?

_____

Problems 4 and 5: Write your multiple-choice answer in the space provided.

4. The name given to triangle LMN is

_____

a) equilateral
b) isosceles
c) right
d) scalene

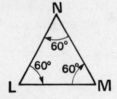

5. The name given to triangle XYZ is

_____

a) equilateral
b) isosceles
c) right
d) scalene

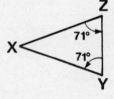

6. Solve for d:
$$\frac{10}{17} = \frac{d}{51}$$

_____

7. Triangles CDE and RST are similar triangles. What is the length of side CD in triangle CDE?

_____

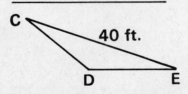

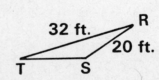

8. In triangle ABC, $\angle A = 122°$ and $\angle B = 30°$.
    In triangle DEF, $\angle D = 50°$ and $\angle E = 122°$.
    Is triangle ABC similar to triangle DEF?

    _____

9. To measure the distance across Blue River Canyon,
    Lucy measured the distances as shown on the drawing
    below. Use her drawing to determine the distance (*d*)
    across the canyon.

    _____

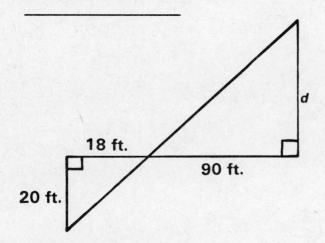

10. George is 6 feet tall and his shadow measured 8 feet
    long at noon. At the same time, a nearby flagpole cast
    a 40-foot shadow. What is the height of the flagpole?

    _____

11. Find the square of each number below.
    a) $2^2 =$ _____   c) $6^2 =$ _____
    b) $4^2 =$ _____   d) $8^2 =$ _____

12. Find the square root of each number below.
    a) $\sqrt{9} =$ _____   c) $\sqrt{49} =$ _____
    b) $\sqrt{36} =$ _____   d) $\sqrt{81} =$ _____

13. What is the length of the hypotenuse of the triangle at the right?

_____

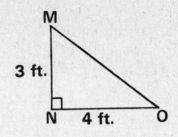

14. A 13-foot ramp is attached to a 5-foot-high loading dock. How far is the bottom of the ramp from the dock?

_____

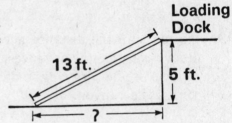

15. One side of a right triangle measures 8 feet. The other side measures 6 feet. What is the length of the hypotenuse?

_____

FINAL TRIANGLES INVENTORY CHART

Circle the number of any problem that you missed and be sure to review the appropriate page. A passing score is 12 correct answers. If you miss more than three questions, you should review this chapter.

Problem	Skill Area	Page
1	sum of angles	36
2	sum of angles: applying skills	38
3	sum of angles	36
4	definitions of triangles	40
5	definitions of triangles	40
6	similar triangles: proportion	46
7	similar triangles	48
8	similar triangles	44
9	similar triangles: applying skills	52
10	similar triangles: applying skills	52
11	squares	54
12	square roots	55
13	Pythagorean Theorem	56
14	Pythagorean Theorem: applying skills	60
15	Pythagorean Theorem	56

PLANE FIGURES

PLANE FIGURES SKILLS INVENTORY

This inventory will let you know what you need to work on in the PLANE FIGURES section of _Number Power: Geometry_.

Do all of the following problems that you can. Work carefully and check all your answers. On this inventory, you can use the $\frac{22}{7}$ form of π.

1. _Add_: 5 ft. 9 in.
            7 ft. 8 in.
            3 ft. 6 in.

2. _Add_: 8 m 95 cm
            2 m 45 cm
            6 m 75 cm

3. _Subtract_: 9 yds. 1 ft.
                4 yds. 2 ft.

4. _Subtract_: 3 km 850 m
                1 km 975 m

5. _Multiply_: 7 yds. 2 ft.
                          9

6. _Multiply_: 5 cm 4 mm
                        6

7. _Divide_: 5)8 yds. 1 ft.

8. A blueprint calls for 175 feet of electrical wire. Is a roll containing 56 yards of wire long enough?

9. Harlan is installing a rain gutter along a 54-foot section of roof. He decides to do the job by using five sections of gutter placed end-to-end. If each section measures 12 feet 8 inches long, how much gutter will he have left over?

In problems 10-15, name each of the figures shown.

10. _____   11. _____   12. _____

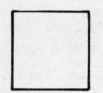

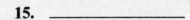

13. _____   14. _____   15. _____

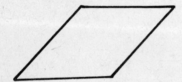

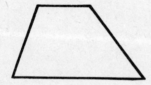

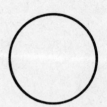

16. Match each formula on the left with the area it represents on the right.

_____ 1) $\frac{1}{2}bh$ a) area of a trapezoid

_____ 2) πr^2 b) area of a rectangle

_____ 3) bh c) area of a square

_____ 4) lw d) area of a triangle

_____ 5) $\frac{1}{2}(b_1 + b_2)h$ e) area of a parallelogram

_____ 6) s^2 f) area of a circle

In problems 17-22, find the perimeter and area of each figure.

17. P = _____

    A = _____

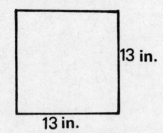

13 in.

13 in.

18. P = _____

    A = _____

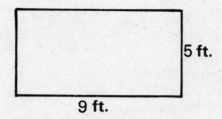

5 ft.

9 ft.

19. P = _____

    A = _____

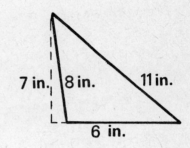

7 in. | 8 in. | 11 in.

6 in.

20. P = _____

    A = _____

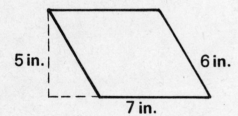

5 in. | 6 in.

7 in.

21. P = _____

    A = _____

3 ft.

6 ft. | 4 ft. | 5 ft.

7 ft.

22. C = _____

    A = _____

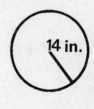

14 in.

23. Edna's garden is in the shape of a rectangle having sides 35 meters and 21 meters. How much fencing material will it take to enclose the garden?

_____

24. Bill has a circular swimming pool that has a radius of 7 feet. What is the approximate surface area of the pool?

_____

25. What is the floor area of the L-shaped room pictured below?

_____

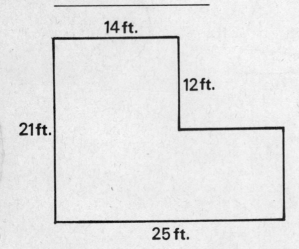

PLANE FIGURES INVENTORY CHART

Use this inventory to see what you already know about plane figures and what you need to work on. A passing score is 21 correct answers. Even if you have a passing score, circle the number of any problem that you miss, correct it, and turn to the practice page indicated.

Problem	Skill Area	Page
1	addition: English units	74
2	addition: metric units	74
3	subtraction: English units	74
4	subtraction: metric units	74
5	multiplication: English units	76
6	multiplication: metric units	76
7	division: English units	76
8	length units: applying skills	78
9	length units: applying skills	78
10	recognizing polygons	82
11	recognizing polygons	82
12	recognizing polygons	82
13	recognizing polygons	82
14	recognizing polygons	82
15	circles	102
16	formulas	106
17	square: perimeter + area	86+88
18	rectangle: perimeter + area	90+92
19	triangle: perimeter + area	94+96
20	parallelogram: perimeter + area	98
21	trapezoid: perimeter + area	98
22	circle: circumference + area	102+104
23	perimeter + area: applying skills	106
24	perimeter + area: applying skills	106
25	two-step area problems	110

WORKING WITH ENGLISH LENGTH UNITS

In the United States, we generally use the _English System_ of measurement. The familiar units of length are summarized below.

Unit	Abbreviation	Examples	Relation to Other Units
inch	in. or "	5 in. or 5"	1 inch = $\frac{1}{12}$ foot
foot	ft. or '	7 ft. or 7'	1 foot = 12 inches
			1 foot = $\frac{1}{3}$ yard
yard	yd.	9 yds.	1 yard = 36 inches
			1 yard = 3 feet
mile	mi.	12 mi.	1 mile = 5,280 feet
			1 mile = 1,760 yards

A given length can be written in more than one way. Examples 1 and 2 below show the use of multiplication to _convert_ (change) a larger unit to a smaller unit.

EXAMPLE 1: Express 6 yards in feet.

  Step 1. Write the problem:
  6 yards = _____ feet

  Step 2. You can substitute 3 feet for the word yards since 1 yard = 3 feet. Multiply.
  *6 (3 feet) = 18 feet

  Answer: 18 feet

EXAMPLE 2: Express 7 feet in inches.

  Step 1. Write the problem:
  7 feet = _____ inches

  Step 2. You can substitute 12 inches for the word feet since 1 foot = 12 inches. Multiply.
  *7 (12 in.) = 84 in.

  Answer: 84 inches

* Note: In geometry and algebra, multiplication is often indicated by parentheses (without the multiplication sign "✕").

Change each larger length unit to the smaller unit indicated.

Examples:
  8 ft. = 8 (12 in.)
     = **96 in.**

  7 yds. = 7 (3 ft.)
      = **21 ft.**

  3 mi. = 3 (5,280 ft.)
      = **15,840 ft.**

  2 mi. = 2 (1,760 yds.)
      = **3,520 yds.**

1. 13 ft. = _____ in.   4 ft. = _____ in.

2. 9 yds. = _____ ft.   16 yds. = _____ ft.

3. 4 mi. = _____ ft.   2 mi. = _____ ft.

4. 3 mi. = _____ yds.   5 mi. = _____ yds.

As shown in Examples 3 and 4 below, a length is often simplified by expressing it in the largest possible whole number length units.

EXAMPLE 3: Write 17 in. as feet and inches.

Step 1. Write the problem:
17 in. = _____ ft. _____ in.

Step 2. Multiply to change inches to feet.
Since 1 inch = $\frac{1}{12}$ foot, you multiply 17 by $(\frac{1}{12})$.
$$17(\tfrac{1}{12}) = \tfrac{17}{12} = 1\tfrac{5}{12} \text{ ft.}$$

Note: $\frac{5}{12}$ ft. = 5 in.
Thus, $1\frac{5}{12}$ ft. = **1 ft. 5 in.**

Answer: **17 in. = 1 ft. 5 in.**

EXAMPLE 4: Simplify 4 ft. 27 in.

Step 1. Change 27 in. to ft. and in. by multiplying by $\frac{1}{12}$.
$$27 \text{ in.} = 27(\tfrac{1}{12}) = \tfrac{27}{12} \text{ ft.}$$
$$= 2\tfrac{3}{12} \text{ ft.}$$
$$= 2 \text{ ft. } 3 \text{ in.}$$

Step 2. Add 2 ft. 3 in. to 4 ft.

        4 ft.
    +2 ft. 3 in.
      6 ft. 3 in.

Answer: **4 ft. 27 in. = 6 ft. 3 in.**

Simplify each length below.

Examples:

21 in. = 21 $(\frac{1}{12}$ ft.) =
   $1\frac{9}{12}$ ft. = **1 ft. 9 in.**

7 ft. = 7 $(\frac{1}{3}$ yds.) =
   $2\frac{1}{3}$ yds. = **2 yds. 1 ft.**

1,900 yds. = 1,900 $(\frac{1}{1,760}$ mi.) =
$\frac{1,900}{1,760}$ mi. = **1 mi. 140 yds.**

5 ft. 15 in. =   5 ft.
           + 1 ft. 3 in.
             6 ft. 3 in.

3 yds. 7 ft. =   3 yds.
           +2 yds. 1 ft.
            5 yds. 1 ft.

1 mi. 6,000 ft. =   1 mi.
             +1 mi. 720 ft.
              2 mi. 720 ft.

5. 19 in. = _____   31 in. = _____

6. 11 ft. = _____   8 ft. = _____

7. 2,100 yds. = _____   3,100 yds. = _____

8. 6 ft. 17 in. = _____   7 ft. 23 in. _____

9. 5 yds. 8 ft. = _____   11 yds. 13 ft. = _____

10. 1 mi. 8,000 ft. =   1 mi. 10,280 ft. =

    _____   _____

WORKING WITH METRIC LENGTH UNITS

Most of the countries of the world use the *Metric System* of measurement. This system is slowly becoming more popular in the United States and is now being taught in many schools along with the familiar English System.

The length units of the Metric System are summarized below.

Unit	Abbreviation	Example	Relation to Other Units
millimeter	mm	8 mm	1 millimeter = .1 centimeter
centimeter	cm	11 cm	1 centimeter = 10 millimeters
meter	m	63 m	1 meter = 100 centimeters
kilometer	km	5 km	1 kilometer = 1,000 meters

To get a "feeling" for the size of metric units, compare each with a familiar English unit:

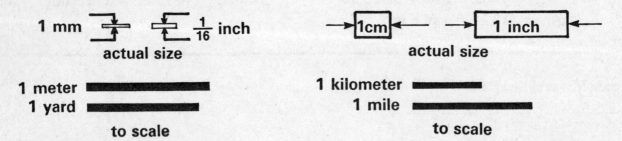

The decimal (10, 100, 1,000) relation between units in the Metric System makes it easier to work with metric units than with English units.

For example, to change a length from a larger unit to a smaller unit, replace the larger unit with the equivalent number of smaller units and multiply.

EXAMPLES: 2 cm = 2 (10 mm) = 20 mm—since there are 10 mm in a centimeter.
5 m = 5 (100 cm) = 500 cm—since there are 100 cm in a meter.
3 km = 3 (1,000 m) = 3,000 m—since there are 1,000 m in a kilometer.

Change each larger length unit to the smaller unit indicated.

Examples:

3 cm = 3 (10 mm)
= **30 mm**

8 m = 8 (100 cm)
= **800 cm**

2 km = 2 (1,000 m)
= **2,000 m**

1. 9 cm = _____ mm   4 cm = _____ mm   6 cm = _____ mm

2. 7 m = _____ cm   9 m = _____ cm   5 m = _____ cm

3. 7 km = _____ m   10 km = _____ m   4 km = _____ m

As the following three rules show, simplifying lengths in the Metric System is easier than in the English System.

Rule 1. To simplify 10 or more millimeters, write the number in the 10's place as the number of centimeters.

EXAMPLE: 14 millimeters = 1 centimeter 4 millimeters
↳ *number in 10's place*

Rule 2. To simplify 100 or more centimeters, write the number in the 100's place as the number of meters.

EXAMPLE: 346 centimeters = 3 meters 46 centimeters
↳ *number in 100's place*

Rule 3. To simplify 1,000 or more meters, write the number to the left of the 100's place as the number of kilometers.

EXAMPLE: 12,450 meters = 12 kilometers 450 meters
↳ *number to the left of 100's place*

Use these rules to simplify more complicated lengths as follows:

EXAMPLE 1: Simplify 7 cm 29 mm.

Step 1. Write 29 mm as cm and mm.
Use **Rule 1**:
29 mm = 2 cm 9 mm

Step 2. Add the 2 cm 9 mm to the 7 cm.

```
  7 cm
+ 2 cm 9 mm
  9 cm 9 mm
```

Answer: 7 cm 29 mm = 9 cm 9 mm

EXAMPLE 2: Simplify 9 m 368 cm.

Step 1. Write 368 cm as m and cm
Use **Rule 2**:
368 cm = 3 m 68 cm

Step 2. Add the 3 m 68 cm to the 9 m.

```
   9 m
+  3 m 68 cm
  12 m 68 cm
```

Answer: 9 m 368 cm = 12 m 68 cm

Simplify each length below.

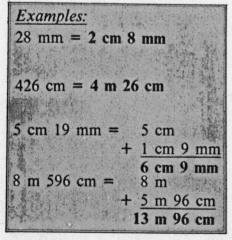

Examples:
28 mm = 2 cm 8 mm

426 cm = 4 m 26 cm

```
5 cm 19 mm =   5 cm
            + 1 cm 9 mm
              6 cm 9 mm
```

```
8 m 596 cm =   8 m
            + 5 m 96 cm
             13 m 96 cm
```

4. 79 mm = _____   83 mm = _____

5. 748 cm = _____   104 cm = _____

6. 7 cm 57 mm = _____   9 cm 39 mm = _____

7. 5 m 856 cm = _____   12 m 800 cm = _____

ADDITION AND SUBTRACTION OF LENGTH UNITS

To add two or more lengths, add the number of each length unit separately and then simplify the answer. An example is shown below both for lengths in the English System and lengths in the Metric System.

ENGLISH SYSTEM

Add: 6 ft. 8 in.
         3 ft. 6 in.
         <u>4 ft. 3 in.</u>
      13 ft. 17 in.

Answer: **14 ft. 5 in.**
(Since 17 in. = 1 ft. 5 in.)

METRIC SYSTEM

Add: 7 cm 9 mm
         4 cm 4 mm
         <u>5 cm 8 mm</u>
      16 cm 21 mm

Answer: **18 cm 1mm**
(Since 21 mm = 2 cm 1 mm)

Addition

Step 1. Add each column separately.
Step 2. Simplify the sum.

To subtract one length from another, subtract each length unit separately, starting with the unit in the right-hand column. Borrowing is often necessary in subtraction and is illustrated in both the English and the Metric examples below.

Subtraction

Step 1. If necessary, borrow 1 whole unit from the left column. Add this borrowed unit to the right column.

Step 2. Subtract each column.

Subtract: 5 ft. 2 in.
          <u>3 ft. 9 in.</u>

Borrow: 1 ft. = 12 in.
        (12 in. + 2 in.
        = 14 in.)

Write: $\overset{4}{\cancel{5}}$ ft. $\overset{14}{\cancel{2}}$ in.
        <u>3 ft. 9 in.</u>

Answer: **1 ft. 5 in.**

Subtract: 8 cm 5 mm
          <u>4 cm 8 mm</u>

Borrow: 1 cm = 10 mm
        (10 mm + 5 mm
        = 15 mm)

Write: $\overset{7}{\cancel{8}}$ cm $\overset{15}{\cancel{5}}$ mm
        <u>4 cm 8 mm</u>

Answer: **3 cm 7 mm**

Add the following lengths and simplify each answer.

Examples:
5 ft. 7 in.
3 ft. 9 in.
8 ft. 16 in. =
9 ft. 4 in.
4 yds. 1 ft.
2 yds. 2 ft.
1 yd. 2 ft.
7 yds. 5 ft. =
8 yds. 2 ft.
5 cm 9 mm
1 cm 2 mm
6 cm 11 mm =
7 cm 1 mm
9 m 57 cm
7 m 40 cm
3 m 60 cm
19 m 157 cm =
20 m 57 cm

1.
7 ft. 8 in.	4 yds. 1 ft.	8 mi. 400 yds.
1 ft. 5 in.	2 yds. 2 ft.	3 mi. 1700 yds.

2.
5 yds. 2 ft.	7 ft. 8 in.	2 yds. 2 ft.
2 yds. 1 ft.	3 ft. 9 in.	3 yds. 1 ft.
4 yds. 2 ft.	5 ft. 3 in.	6 yds.

3.
6 cm 8 mm	9 m 58 cm	2 km 460 m
4 cm 6 mm	1 m 90 cm	3 km 750 m

4.
12 m 75 cm	25 cm 8 mm	5 km 100 m
9 m 80 cm	11 cm 4 mm	3 km 500 m
6 m 35 cm	8 cm 5 mm	2 km 750 m

Subtract the following lengths.

Examples:
⁵   ¹⁷
6 ft. 7 in.
3 ft. 9 in.
2 ft. 8 in.
³   ⁴
4 yds. 1 ft.
2 yds. 2 ft.
1 yd. 2 ft.
⁶   ¹⁸
7 cm 8 mm
3 cm 9 mm
3 cm 9 mm

5.
7 ft. 3 in.	3 yds. 1 ft.	5 ft. 7 in.
4 ft. 8 in.	1 yds. 2 ft.	2 ft. 11 in.

6.
6 yds. 1 ft.	3 ft. 2 in.	7 yds. 1 ft.
1 yd. 2 ft.	1 ft. 9 in.	6 yds. 2 ft.

7.
12 cm 7 mm	35 m 50 cm	9 km 150 m
4 cm 8 mm	17 m 85 cm	3 km 500 m

MULTIPLICATION AND DIVISION OF LENGTH UNITS

To multiply a length by a number, multiply each length unit separately. Then, simplify the answer when possible. The examples below show how this is done.

ENGLISH SYSTEM

Multiply: 3 yds. 2 ft.
$$\underline{\hspace{2.5cm}6\hspace{1cm}}$$
18 yds. 12 ft.

Answer: **22 yds.**
(Since 12 ft. = 4 yds.,
18 yds. + 4 yds. = **22 yds.**)

Multiplication	
Step 1.	Multiply each column.
Step 2.	Simplify the product.

METRIC SYSTEM

Multiply: 8 m 70 cm
$$\underline{\hspace{2.5cm}3\hspace{1cm}}$$
24 m 210 cm

Answer: **26 m 10 cm**
(Since 210 cm = 2 m 10 cm,
24 m + 2 m 10 cm = **26 m 10 cm.**)

To divide a length by a number, first divide the number into the largest length unit. Next, change any remainder into the next smallest unit in the problem. Add the remainder to the number of smaller units in the problem, and then divide this sum by the number. The examples below demonstrate this process.

	Division	
Step 1.	Divide the first column.	
Step 2.	Change the remainder of the first column to the units of the second column. Add this remainder to the second column.	
Step 3.	Add the numbers in the second column. Divide this sum.	

English:

Divide: 1 ft.
$$4\overline{)\,5 \text{ ft. } 8 \text{ in.}}$$
     4
Remainder: 1 ft.
Add: 1 ft. = 12 in. to second column

Answer: **1 ft. 5 in.**
$$4\overline{)\,5 \text{ ft. } 8 \text{ in.}}$$
     4
Divide 20 1 ft.= 12 in.
by 4:   20 in.
          20 in.

Metric:

Divide: 2 m
$$3\overline{)\,7 \text{ m } 92 \text{ cm}}$$
     6
Remainder: 1 m
Add: 1 m = 100 cm to second column

Answer: **2 m 64 cm**
$$3\overline{)\,7 \text{ m } 92 \text{ cm}}$$
     6
Divide 192 1 m = 100 cm
by 3:   192 cm
          192 cm

Multiply each of the following lengths as indicated, and simplify each answer.

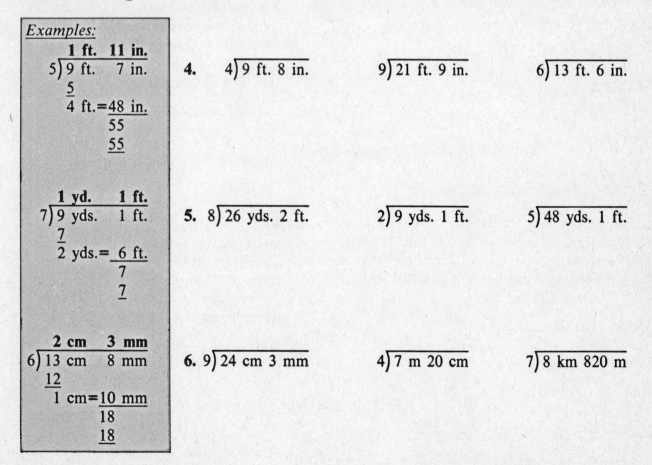

Examples:

```
    6 ft.   9 in.
            3
   18 ft.  27 in.  =
   20 ft.   3 in.
```

1.
```
   7 ft. 6 in.
           8
```
```
   9 yds. 2 ft.
           4
```
```
   2 mi. 400 yds.
              7
```

```
    5 yds.   2 ft.
             7
   35 yds.  14 ft.  =
   39 yds.   2 ft.
```

2.
```
   9 yds. 1 ft.
           8
```
```
   4 ft. 11 in.
          6
```
```
   2 yds. 2 ft.
           9
```

```
    8 cm  9 mm
            6
   48 cm  54 mm  =
   53 cm   4 mm
```

3.
```
   9 cm 4 mm
         7
```
```
   3 cm 8 mm
         5
```
```
   7 m 45 cm
          4
```

Divide each length as indicated.

Examples:

```
         1 ft.   11 in.
    5) 9 ft.     7 in.
       5
       4 ft. = 48 in.
               55
               55
```

4. 4) 9 ft. 8 in.   9) 21 ft. 9 in.   6) 13 ft. 6 in.

```
        1 yd.    1 ft.
   7) 9 yds.   1 ft.
      7
      2 yds. =  6 ft.
                7
                7
```

5. 8) 26 yds. 2 ft.   2) 9 yds. 1 ft.   5) 48 yds. 1 ft.

```
        2 cm     3 mm
   6) 13 cm     8 mm
      12
       1 cm = 10 mm
              18
              18
```

6. 9) 24 cm 3 mm   4) 7 m 20 cm   7) 8 km 820 m

WORKING WITH LENGTH UNITS: APPLYING YOUR SKILLS

Solve the problems below.

1. Bill needs 109 inches of baseboard to place along the family room floor. Will a board that is 8 feet long be enough?

   _____

2. To fence her back yard, Heather estimated it would take 32 yards of fencing material. Will two rolls of fencing be enough if each roll contains a 50-foot length of material?

   _____

3. To make a long garden hose, Leona connected three shorter hoses together. If each of the shorter hoses measures 24 feet 9 inches, what is the length of the combined hose?

   _____

4. Daniel uses gold wire in his jewelry-making business. Of his supply, Daniel has used all but four separate lengths of the precious wire. These lengths measure: 29 cm 9 mm, 11 cm 4 mm, 14 cm 7 mm, and 16 cm 9 mm. If the wire costs $20 per centimeter of length (or $2 per millimeter), what is the value of the wire that Daniel has left?

   _____

5. On Mona's thirteenth birthday, she measured 4 feet 9 inches tall. How much has she grown since her sixth birthday when her height was 3 feet 11 inches?

   _____

6. When Billy was in the 7th grade, he could throw a football 34 yards 2 feet. Now, in the 12th grade, he can throw it 47 yards 1 foot. How much farther can he throw it now than when he was in the 7th grade?

   _____

7. Terry's height is 176 centimeters. His friend, Fred, stands 2 meters 3 centimeters tall. Which boy is taller?

_____

8. To frame a front door, Susy needs three pieces of molding: two pieces measuring 6′ 8″ each, and one piece measuring 3′ 2″. If she cuts these pieces from a board that measures 17′ 2″, how much molding will she have left?

_____

9. Chris entered a 100 km bicycle race. During the first three hours, she rode the following distances: 1st hour = 23 km 800 m, 2nd hour = 25 km 350 m, 3rd hour = 26 km 575 m. After the third hour, how much farther did she still have to ride?

_____

10. Jamie designed a picnic table that requires six 2″ by 6″ boards, each board measuring 6′ 9″ long. What is the total length of 2″ by 6″ boards needed?

_____

11. A quilt pattern calls for four pieces of fabric, each measuring 7 inches long, and four pieces of fabric, each measuring 8 inches long. How much fabric will be left over if all these pieces are cut from a piece that is 6′ 5″ long?

_____

12. Barbara has 25 decorative bricks. Each brick is 14 inches long. If the bricks are placed end-to-end in a straight line, what distance will they cover? Give your answer to the nearest foot.

_____

13. If Vince wants to cut an 8 foot 9 inch pipe into five equal pieces, how long should he cut each piece?

_____

14. Shauna is going to divide a 10 meter long ribbon into four equal lengths. To the nearest centimeter, how long will each smaller ribbon be?

_____

PERIMETER

The distance around a flat (plane) object is known as its _perimeter_. For example, the distance around a field or a lake is called its perimeter. The symbol for perimeter is "P."

Perimeter is measured in length units. To find the perimeter of a many-sided figure, add the lengths of the sides.

EXAMPLE 1: What is the perimeter of the figure at the right?

To find the perimeter, add the lengths of the five sides:

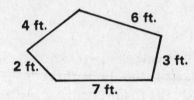

$$\begin{array}{r} 6 \text{ ft.} \\ 3 \text{ ft.} \\ 7 \text{ ft.} \\ 2 \text{ ft.} \\ +4 \text{ ft.} \\ \hline P = 22 \text{ ft.} \end{array}$$

Answer: The perimeter is 22 ft. or 7 yds. 1 ft.

EXAMPLE 2: Find the perimeter of the field at the right. Simplify the answer.

Step 1. Add the lengths of the four sides:

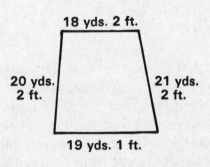

$$\begin{array}{r} 18 \text{ yds. } 2 \text{ ft.} \\ 21 \text{ yds. } 2 \text{ ft.} \\ 19 \text{ yds. } 1 \text{ ft.} \\ +20 \text{ yds. } 2 \text{ ft.} \\ \hline 78 \text{ yds. } 7 \text{ ft.} \end{array}$$

Step 2. Simplify the answer:
a) Change 7 ft. to 2 yds. 1 ft.
b) Add 2 yds. 1 ft. to 78 yds.

$$\begin{array}{r} 78 \text{ yds.} \\ +2 \text{ yds. } 1 \text{ ft.} \\ \hline 80 \text{ yds. } 1 \text{ ft.} \end{array}$$

Answer: The perimeter is 80 yds. 1 ft.

What is the perimeter of each figure below?

1. P = _____

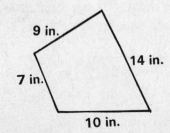

2. P = _____

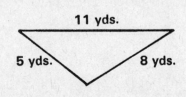

3. P = _____

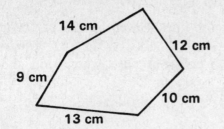

4. P = _____

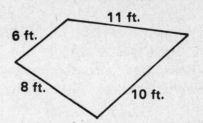

Find the perimeter of each figure below and simplify the answer.

5. P = _____

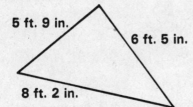

6. P = _____

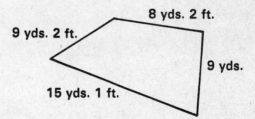

7. P = _____

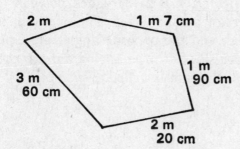

8. P = _____

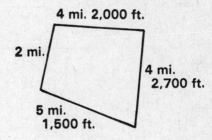

RECOGNIZING COMMON POLYGONS

A *polygon* is a plane (flat) figure formed by three or more lines. Several types of polygons are given special names.

Below are listed the names and descriptions of five polygons with which you should become familiar.

Name	Example	Description

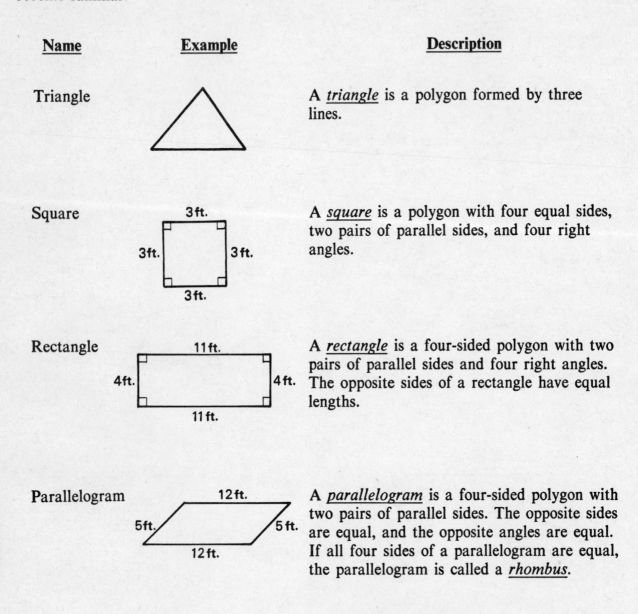

Triangle

A *triangle* is a polygon formed by three lines.

Square

A *square* is a polygon with four equal sides, two pairs of parallel sides, and four right angles.

Rectangle

A *rectangle* is a four-sided polygon with two pairs of parallel sides and four right angles. The opposite sides of a rectangle have equal lengths.

Parallelogram

A *parallelogram* is a four-sided polygon with two pairs of parallel sides. The opposite sides are equal, and the opposite angles are equal. If all four sides of a parallelogram are equal, the parallelogram is called a *rhombus*.

Trapezoid

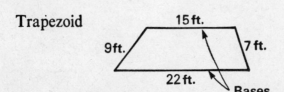

A *trapezoid* is a four-sided polygon with one pair of parallel sides called *bases*. All four sides of a trapezoid can be different lengths.

Label each figure below with its polygon name: triangle, square, rectangle, parallelogram, or trapezoid.

1. _____

2. _____

3. _____

4. _____

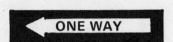

5. _____

6. _____

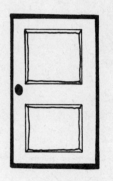

7. _____

Sign

8. _____

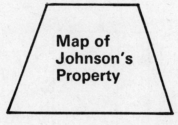

9. _____

Chimney

10. _____

Wedge

11. _____

12. _____

Toy Block

AREA

Area is a measure of surface. A larger surface has a larger area. For example, the total floor area of a house is larger than the area of any one of its rooms. The symbol for area is "A."

To measure area, we use an *area unit* in the shape of a square.

For example, we can use this square 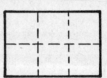 as our area unit.

The surface area of a figure can be measured by the number of square area units that fit inside the figure. One way to find the area is to divide a figure into square area units and then count the units that fit inside the figure.

EXAMPLE: What is the area of the rectangle at right?

The rectangle has been divided into square area units.

To find the area of the rectangle, count the number of area units that fit inside the rectangle.

Answer: A = 6 area units.

What is the area of each figure below? Each figure has been divided into square area units.

1. A = _____ area units   **2.** A = _____ area units   **3.** A = _____ area units

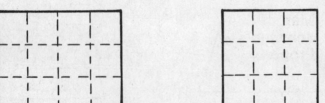

4. A = _____ area units   **5.** A = _____ area units   **6.** A = _____ area units

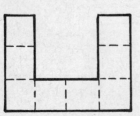
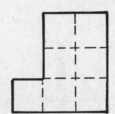
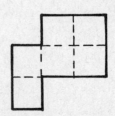

Not all figures can be simply divided into a whole number of square area units. **Find the area of each figure below as accurately as possible.** Some answers will include fractions.

7. A = _____ area units

8. A = _____ area units

9. A = _____ area units

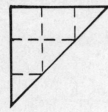

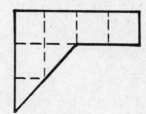

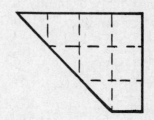

10. A = _____ area units

11. A = _____ area units

12. A = _____ area units

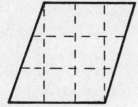

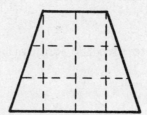

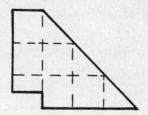

For many curved figures, counting area units gives only an approximate area. **See how accurate you can be in finding the area of the two curved surfaces below.**

13. A = _____ area units

14. A = _____ area units

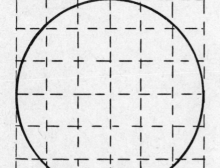

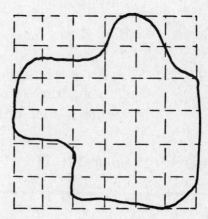

WORKING WITH SQUARES

In the pages ahead, you'll learn to use _formulas_ to find perimeters and areas of common geometrical figures. As you saw in the chapter on triangles, a formula is a rule that uses letters in place of numbers. To use a formula, you replace the letters with numbers and then do the arithmetic.

Perimeter

The sides of a _square_ are all the same length. Because of this, you can write a simple formula for finding the perimeter of a square:

$$P = 4s$$

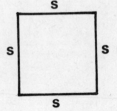

This means that perimeter equals four times s where s is the length of each side.

This formula can be rearranged to give the length of each side when you know the perimeter:

$$s = \frac{P}{4}$$

This means that a side's length is found by dividing the perimeter by four.

EXAMPLE 1:   What is the perimeter of a square that has a side 3 feet long?
Substitute 3 for s in the formula $P = 4s$
$$P = 4 \times 3 = 12$$

3 ft.

Answer: **12 ft. or 4 yds.**

EXAMPLE 2:   What is the length of each side of a square that has a perimeter of 140 inches?
Substitute 140 for P in the formula $s = \frac{P}{4}$
$$s = \frac{140}{4} = 35$$

Answer: **35 in. or 2 ft. 11 in.**

Use the formula P = 4s to find the perimeter of each square below.

1. P = _____

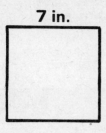

7 in.

2. P = _____

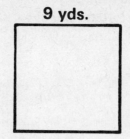

9 yds.

3. P = _____

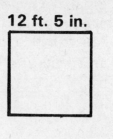

12 ft. 5 in.

4. P = _____

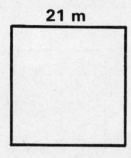

21 m

5. P = _____

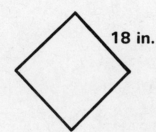

18 in.

6. P = _____

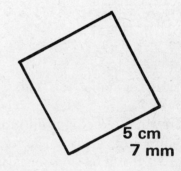

5 cm
7 mm

In problems 7 through 12, find the perimeter or length of one side as requested. Notice that words such as "enclose," "surround," "wrap," and "around" indicate that you are to solve for the perimeter.

7. How much fence material must Bill buy to surround a garden space that is in the shape of a square 17 yards on a side?

   _____

8. Jane wants to make a border for a tablecloth with lace material. How much material will she need if the tablecloth measures 4 feet 4 inches by 4 feet 4 inches?

   _____

9. Michelle runs around a park that has four sides, each measuring 30 feet long. How many times does she have to run around the park to run a total of 1,200 feet?

   _____

10. Allowing 3 feet for the door, how much baseboard would John need to enclose a square room where each wall measures 11 feet?

   _____

11. If the perimeter of a square field measures 440 yards, what is the length of each side?

   _____

12. If the distance around a square room measures 88 feet, what is the length of each side?

   _____

Area Units

The area of common geometrical figures is usually found by using an *area formula*. To use an area formula, substitute numbers for letters and then multiply or divide as indicated. Label your answer with appropriate area units.

Common area units are the following:

English Units	Abbreviation
square inch	sq. in.
square foot	sq. ft.
square yard	sq. yd.
square mile	sq. mi.

Metric Units	Abbreviation
square millimeter	mm^2
square centimeter	cm^2
square meter	m^2
square kilometer	km^2

Area Of A Square

The area of a *square* is given by the formula:

$$A = s^2$$

where s stands for "side" and s^2 means $s \times s$.

The drawing at the right illustrates the use of this formula to find the area of a square. The formula means that the area of the square is found by *squaring* a side—multiplying the value of a side times itself. For the square shown here, that means

$$A = 4 \times 4 = 16.$$

Count the number of smaller squares within the larger one. Does this also total 16?

If the area of a square is known, the length of the side can easily be found. The side is equal to the square root of the area:

$$s = \sqrt{A}$$

Try this formula on the square at the right. Notice that the area is 4 square inches. Do you see that the length of each side is 2 inches? ($\sqrt{4} = 2$)

s

(s = 4 ft.)

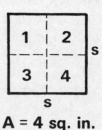

A = 4 sq. in.

EXAMPLE 1:   What is the area of a square that has a side length of 12 meters?

Replace s by 12 in the area formula:

$$A = s^2 = s \times s$$
$$= 12 \times 12 = \textbf{144}$$

Answer: **144 m^2**

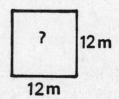

EXAMPLE 2:   What is the length of the side of a square
that has an area of 36 square feet?
To find the length of the side take the
square root of 36.

$$s = \sqrt{36} = 6$$

Answer: 6 feet

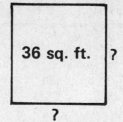

Use the formula $A = s^2$ or $s = \sqrt{A}$ to find the area or the length of the side of each square
below. Be sure that area answers are given in square units.

1. A = _____

2. s = _____

3. A = _____

9 ft.

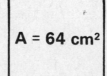

A = 64 cm²

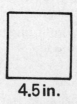

4.5 in.

In problems 4 through 8, find the area or the length of a side as requested. Notice that words
such as "covering," "surface," and "space" are often used to indicate area.

4.   Bill is covering a square table with glass. How much glass
will be needed if the table measures 30 centimeters on each
side?

_____

5.   How much tile will be needed to cover a square utility room
that is 8 feet on each side?

_____

6.   What is the length of each side of a square tablecloth that
covers a surface of 9 square feet?

_____

7.   Find the space of a square garden that is 17 yards on a side.

_____

8.   A square table is to be covered with small square ceramic
tiles. The table has an area of 4 square feet. How many
tiles are needed if each tile measures 3 inches on one side?

_____

WORKING WITH RECTANGLES

Perimeter

The perimeter of a *rectangle* is found by adding the four sides:

$$P = l + w + l + w$$

where *l* stands for "length" and *w* stands for "width."

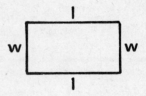

This formula is most often simplified by combining the "*l*'s" and combining the "*w*'s":

$$P = 2l + 2w$$

This means that the perimeter is equal to twice the length plus twice the width.

Note: When multiplication and addition occur in the same problem, do the multiplication first.

EXAMPLE: What is the perimeter of a rectangle that has a length of 8 feet and a width of 5 feet?

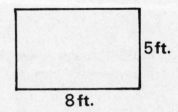

Substitute 8 for "*l*" and 5 for "*w*" in the perimeter formula:

$$P = 2l + 2w$$
$$P = (2 \times 8) + (2 \times 5)$$
$$= 16 + 10$$
$$= 26$$

Answer: The perimeter is 26 ft. or 8 yds. 2 ft.

Use the formula P = 2l + 2w to find the perimeter of each rectangle below.

1. P = _____   **2.** P = _____   **3.** P = _____

9 yds. — 4 yds.

13 ft. — 21 ft.

3 ft. 9 in. — 3 ft. 4 in.

4. P = _____

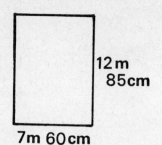

12 m
85 cm

7m 60 cm

5. P = _____

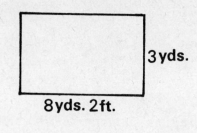

3 yds.

8 yds. 2 ft.

6. P = _____

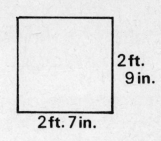

2 ft.
9 in.

2 ft. 7 in.

7. How many feet of fencing material will Louise need to surround her garden that measures 15 feet 8 inches on two sides and 19 feet 10 inches on the other two sides?

_____

8. After adding 4 extra inches for each corner, how much molding will Jim need to enclose a window that measures 36 inches by 40 inches?

_____

9. Julie plans to add a lace edge to her bedspread which is in the shape of a rectangle. How much lace will she need if the bedspread measures 6 ft. by 5 ft. 8 in.?

_____

10. A rectangular field measures 100 yards by 76 yards. How many laps around the field does Len have to run in order to run one mile? (1 mile = 1,760 yards)

_____

11. Determine the perimeter of a lawn which is in the shape of a rectangle and measures 35 meters 50 centimeters by 48 meters 25 centimeters?

_____

12. Subtracting 2 feet 11 inches for door space, how much baseboard would be needed to go around a rectangular room that measures 11 feet 4 inches by 12 feet 7 inches?

_____

Area

The area of a *rectangle* is given by the formula:

$$A = lw$$

where *l* stands for "length" and *w* stands for "width."

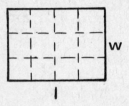

In geometry and algebra, two letters standing side by side indicate multiplication.

The rectangle above is an illustration of the use of the area formula. The area is easily found by counting the area units (12) or by multiplying the length (4) by the width (3): $4 \times 3 = 12$.

The area formula can be rewritten so that a side can be found if the area is given. Because you multiply the sides to find the area, you can divide the area by one side to find the second side. The formula for finding the length or the width is either:

$$l = \frac{A}{w} \text{ or } w = \frac{A}{l}$$

These formulas show that one side is equal to the area divided by the second side.

EXAMPLE 1: What is the area of a rectangle that has a length of 5 feet and a width of 4 feet?

To find the area, multiply the length (5) by the width (4):

$$A = 5 \times 4 = 20$$

Answer: **20 square feet**

EXAMPLE 2: What is the width of a rectangle that has an area of 48 square yards and a length of 12 yards?

To find the width, divide the area (48) by the length (12):

$$w = \frac{48}{12} = 4$$

Answer: **4 yards**

Note: Area is given in square units but a side is not.

Use the formula A = *lw* or l = $\frac{A}{w}$ (or w = $\frac{A}{l}$) to find the area or length (width) of each rectangle below.

1. A = _____

9 ft.

13 ft.

2. A = _____

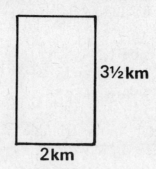

3½ km

2 km

3. w = _____

A = 136 sq. in.

17 in.

4. A = _____

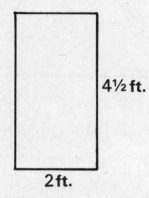

4½ ft.

2 ft.

5. l = _____

A = 45.5 cm²

5 cm

6. A = _____

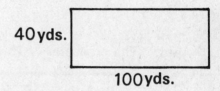

40 yds.

100 yds.

7. Brenda found that a bedroom floor measures 5 yards long and 4½ yards wide. How many square yards of carpet would she need to cover this floor?

_____

8. How many square feet of tile are needed to put a new tile surface on an outdoor patio that measures 32 feet by 20 feet?

_____

9. The label on a gallon of interior wall paint reads: "Coverage: 400 square feet." If a wall is 8 feet high, what maximum length of wall could be painted by 1½ gallons?

_____

10. A standard piece of typing paper measures 11 inches long by 8½ inches wide. Is the area of a piece of this paper larger than 100 square inches?

_____

11. A window measures 2¼ feet high and 4 feet wide. How many square feet of glass will be needed to replace the broken window?

_____

12. Find the width of a field that has an area of 6,000 square meters and a length of 120 meters.

_____

WORKING WITH TRIANGLES

Perimeter

The perimeter of a _triangle_ is found by adding its three sides:

$$P = s_1 + s_2 + s_3$$

where s_1 stands for "side 1,"
s_2 stands for "side 2," and
s_3 stands for "side 3."

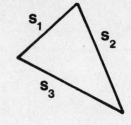

EXAMPLE: What is the perimeter of a triangle that measures 5 feet by 3 feet by 7 feet?

To find the perimeter, add the three sides:

```
   5
   3
 + 7
 ──
  15
```

Answer: The perimeter is 15 feet or 5 yards.

What is the perimeter of each triangle below?

1. P = _____

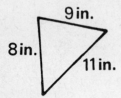

2. P = _____

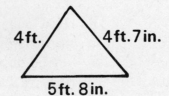

3. P = _____

4. P = _____

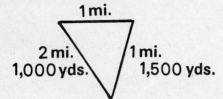

5. P = _____

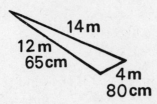

6. P = _____

7. A garden in the shape of a triangle has sides with lengths 18 yards, 27 yards, and 38 yards. How much fencing material will it take to enclose it?

_____

8. A roof gable is in the shape of a triangle. If each of two sides is 18 feet 6 inches and the third side is 38 feet 8 inches, what is the perimeter of the gable?

_____

9. What is the distance around a triangular lot that measures 126 meters by 236 meters by 202 meters?

_____

10. A triangular mirror has three equal sides. Each side measures 8 inches. Allowing three extra inches for each corner, how much molding will be needed to enclose it?

_____

11. A jogging trail has sides that measure 168 yards 2 feet, 175 yards, and 96 yards 1 foot. How many laps around the trail is equal to 1 mile (1,760 yards)?

_____

12. A triangular piece of cut glass is to be enclosed in a solder strip. What length of solder is needed if the glass has sides measuring 4 cm 3 mm, 5 cm 6 mm, and 13 cm 3 mm?

_____

13. Joe's Deli has windows in the shape of triangles. How much molding is needed to enclose 5 windows if a window measures 1 foot 7 inches on each side?

_____

14. Joyce has 15 feet of lace for a border. How much lace will she have left if she puts a border on a triangular tablecloth that has sides of 4 feet 6 inches each?

_____

Area

The area of a *triangle* is given by the formula:

$$A = \tfrac{1}{2} bh$$

where *b* stands for "base" and *h* stands for "height."

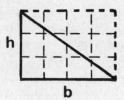

Note: 1) When working with triangles, it is common to talk of "base" and "height" instead of "length" and "width."

2) As the drawing at right shows, the area of a triangle is equal to $\frac{1}{2}$ the area of a rectangle with length "b" and width "h."

The area formula is also used to find the area of triangles that do not contain a right angle.

The area of △ABC is equal to $\frac{1}{2}$ times the base (AC) times the height (BD). Notice that the height BD is not one of the sides of △ABC. The height BD is drawn in to show the distance between the vertex point B and the base AC.

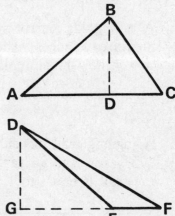

The area of △ DEF is equal to $\frac{1}{2}$ times the base (EF) times the height (DG). Since the vertex point D does not lie directly over the base EF, extend the base EF to point G. The height is then the line DG.

Note: In each case above, the height that appears in the formula is a line *perpendicular* to the base or to its extension. Perpendicular lines meet at right angles.

EXAMPLE 1: What is the area of the triangle at right?

Step 1. Identify the base (*b*) and the height (*h*).

$$b = 12'' \text{ and } h = 8''$$

Step 2. Substitute 12 for *b* and 8 for *h* in the area formula.

$$A = \tfrac{1}{2} bh$$
$$A = \tfrac{1}{2} \times 12 \times 8$$
$$A = 48$$

Answer: **The area is 48 square inches.**

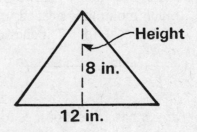

Note: The height does not need to be one of the sides of the triangle.

EXAMPLE 2: What is the area of triangle QRS?

Step 1. Identify the base (*b*) and the height (*h*). Side RS is the base and the dotted line QT is the height.

$b = 3'$ and $h = 5'$

Step 2. Substitute 3 for *b* and 5 for *h* in the area formula.

$A = \frac{1}{2} bh$

$A = \frac{1}{2} \times 3 \times 5$

$= \frac{15}{2} = 7\frac{1}{2}$

Answer: The area is $7\frac{1}{2}$ square feet.

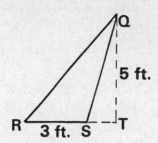

Note: The line drawn to show height may lie outside the triangle.

Use the formula $A = \frac{1}{2} bh$ to find the area of each triangle below.

1. A = _____

2. A = _____

3. A = _____

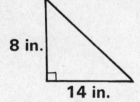

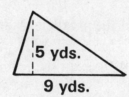

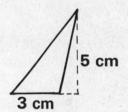

4. A corner of a counter top is shaped like a right triangle. The two sides forming the right angle have lengths of 3 feet and $5\frac{1}{2}$ feet. What is the surface area of this counter?

_____

5. Jim cut a piece of plywood into the shape of a triangle. To the nearest square foot, find the area of the plywood if the base measures 8 feet and the height measures $6\frac{1}{4}$ feet.

_____

6. A seamstress has a piece of cloth left over that is in the shape of an isosceles right triangle. How many square yards of cloth are in the piece if each of the two equal sides measures 3 yards? (*Hint:* The equal sides meet at a right angle.)

_____

WORKING WITH PARALLELOGRAMS AND TRAPEZOIDS

Perimeter

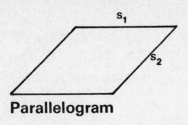

Parallelogram

The perimeter of a _parallelogram_ is given by the formula.
$$P = 2s_1 + 2s_2$$
where s_1 stands for "side 1"
and s_2 stands for "side 2."

> **Note:** s_1 and s_2 are sides that are not parallel. Like a rectangle, the parallel sides have equal lengths.

The perimeter of a _trapezoid_ is found by adding its four sides:
$$P = s_1 + s_2 + s_3 + s_4$$

where s_1 stands for "side 1"
s_2 stands for "side 2"
s_3 stands for "side 3"
s_4 stands for "side 4."

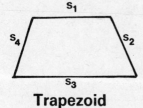

Trapezoid

EXAMPLE 1: What is the perimeter of the parallelogram pictured at the right?

Substitute 7 for s_1 and 4 for s_2 in the formula:
$P = 2s_1 + 2s_2$
$P = (2 \times 7) + (2 \times 4)$
$\quad = 14 + 8 = \mathbf{22}$

**Answer: The perimeter is 22 feet
or 7 yards 1 foot.**

EXAMPLE 2: What is the perimeter of the trapezoid shown at the right?

To find the perimeter, add the four sides of the trapezoid:

$$
\begin{array}{r}
8' \\
6' \\
9' \\
+\ 5' \\
\hline
28' \\
\end{array}
$$

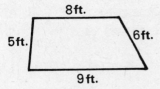

**Answer: The perimeter is 28′
or 9 yards 1 foot.**

What is the perimeter of each figure below?

1. P = _____

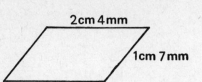

2. P = _____

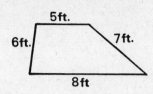

3. P = _____

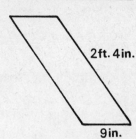

4. P = _____

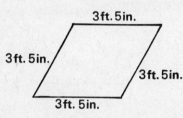

5. P = _____

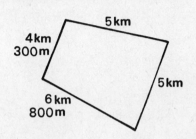

6. P = _____

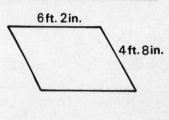

7. Dino's restaurant has a neon sign in the shape of a parallelogram. How much tubing does Dino need to enclose the sign in a neon edge if the sign has side lengths of 4 ft. 5 in. and 3 ft. 8 in.?

_____

8. Joan's lot is in the shape of a trapezoid. What is the perimeter of the lot if the sides measure 79 m 85 cm, 68 m 50 cm, 73 m 60 cm, and 62 m 20 cm?

_____

9. How much fencing will it take to enclose a garden that is shaped like a trapezoid if the sides measure 80 ft., 67 ft., 70 ft., and 61 ft.?

_____

10. A four-sided lot measures 235 yards 2 feet by 208 yards 1 foot by 225 yards by 211 yards. How many laps around the lot are equivalent to 2 miles?

_____

11. How much molding is needed to go around a parallelogram-shaped window that measures 1 m 90 cm along one side and 1 m 6 cm along the other?

_____

12. What is the distance around a rhombus, each side measuring 1 ft. 4 in.? (Remember, a rhombus is a parallelogram that has four sides of the same length.)

_____

Area

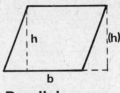

Parallelogram

The area of a *parallelogram* is given by the formula:
$$A = bh$$
where b stands for "base" and h stands for "height."

> **Note:** 1) The *base* is one of the sides on the top or the bottom.
> 2) The *height* is the direct distance between the base and its opposite side. As pictured, the height may be measured inside the parallelogram or outside by dropping a line from the top and extending the base if necessary.

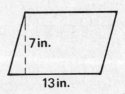

EXAMPLE 1: What is the area of the parallelogram pictured to the right?

Step 1. Identify the base (b) and the height (h).
$$b = 13 \text{ and } h = 7$$

Step 2. Substitute 13 for b and 7 for h in the area formula.
$$A = bh$$
$$A = 13 \times 7 = \mathbf{91}$$

Answer: **The area is 91 square inches.**

The area of a *trapezoid* is given by the formula:

$$A = \tfrac{1}{2}(b_1 + b_2)h$$

where b_1 stands for "base #1"
b_2 stands for "base #2"
h stands for "height"

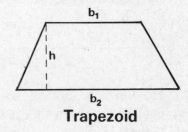

Trapezoid

> **Note:** 1) The *bases* are the pair of parallel sides.
> 2) The *height* is the direct distance between the bases.

EXAMPLE 2: What is the area of the trapezoid pictured at right?

Step 1. Identify b_1 and b_2 and h.
$$b_1 = 6 \text{ and } b_2 = 9 \text{ and } h = 5$$

Step 2. Substitute 6 for b_1, 9 for b_2, and 5 for h in the area formula.
$$A = \tfrac{1}{2} \times (6 + 9) \times 5$$

> **Note:** To evaluate a formula that contains parentheses, add the numbers inside the parentheses *before* multiplying. Step 3 on the next page illustrates this.

Step 3. Add the numbers inside the parentheses before multiplying.

$$A = \tfrac{1}{2} \times (15) \times 5$$

Now, remove the parentheses and multiply.

$$A = \tfrac{1}{2} \times 15 \times 5$$
$$= \frac{15 \times 5}{2}$$
$$= \frac{75}{2}$$
$$= 37\tfrac{1}{2}$$

Answer: The area is $37\tfrac{1}{2}$ square feet.

What is the area of each figure below?

1. A = _____

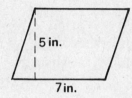

7 in.   5 in.

2. A = _____

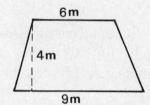

6 m   4 m   9 m

3. A = _____

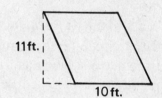

11 ft.   10 ft.

4. The basement of Stephen White's house is in the shape of a
trapezoid. What is the area of the basement if the parallel
sides have lengths of 38 feet and 34 feet, and the distance
between these parallel sides is 22 feet?

_____

5. A playground in the city park is shaped like a parallelogram. If the base measures 35 meters, and the height
measures 27 meters, what is the area of this playground?

_____

6. The Jones's Roofing Co. is going to shingle a section of roof
that is in the shape of a trapezoid. The parallel sides
measure 54 feet and 46 feet, and are 24 feet apart. If a bag
of shingles covers 50 square feet, how many bags of shingles
are needed to cover this roof?

_____

WORKING WITH CIRCLES

As you know, the curved figure to the right is a *circle*.

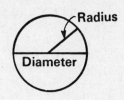

All points on the outside of a circle are at an equal distance from the center. This distance is called the *radius*. The symbol for radius is "r."

The *diameter* is the distance across the circle. As you can see, the diameter passes through the center of the circle, and is equal to twice the radius. The symbol for diameter is "*d*."

In symbols we write: $d = 2r$ or $r = \frac{1}{2}d$.

The distance around the circle is called the *circumference*. The symbol for circumference is "C."

Circumference

The circumference of a circle is given by a formula:

$$C = \pi d$$

π has the approximate value of 3.14 or $3\frac{1}{7}$, usually written as $\frac{22}{7}$.

To find the circumference, multiply the value of π by the diameter. Use the π value $\frac{22}{7}$ when the diameter is given as a whole number or fraction. Use the π value 3.14 when the diameter is given as a mixed decimal.

EXAMPLE 1: Find the circumference of a circle that has a diameter of 14 inches.

Find the circumference by multiplying $\frac{22}{7}$ by 14.

$$\frac{22}{7} \times 14^2 = 44$$

Answer: 44 inches or 3 feet 8 inches

EXAMPLE 2: Find the circumference of a circle that has a diameter of 9.1 feet.

Find the circumference by multiplying 3.14 by 9.1.

$$3.14 \times 9.1 = 28.574$$

Answer: 28.574 feet rounded off to 28.6 feet

Use the formula $C = \pi d$ to find the circumference of each circle below. **Round off decimal answers to a single decimal place.**

1. C = _____

2. C = _____

3. C = _____

In problems 4, 5, and 6, find the diameter (d = 2r) as your first step

4. C = _____   5. C = _____   6. C = _____

In problems 7 through 12, find the circumference.   Notice that the words "distance across" are often used to indicate diameter, and the words "distance from center to edge" and "half the distance across" are used to indicate radius.

7.   Green Reservoir is in the shape of a circle. If the distance across the reservoir is 4 miles, what is its circumference?

_____

8.   The distance between the center and the edge of a circular race track is .2 miles. What is the distance around the track?

_____

9.   To the nearest foot, what is the circumference of a circular swimming pool that has a radius of 6 feet?

_____

10.   Bill measured the widest distance across the top of a circular can to be 14 centimeters. What is the distance around the rim of the can?

_____

11.   Kelly plans to add a border around her circular tablecloth. How long a piece does she need if the diameter of the tablecloth is 4.5 feet?

_____

12.   Half the distance across a circular garden measures 7 meters. How many meters of fencing material will be needed to enclose the garden?

_____

Area

The area of a *circle* is given by a formula:
$$A = \pi r^2 \text{ which means } A = \pi \times r \times r.$$

To find the area of a circle, multiply the radius times itself and then multiply this product by π. As a first step, write the three numbers separated by times signs to see if cancellation is possible. Cancellation can greatly simplify multiplication.

EXAMPLE 1: What is the area of a circle that has a radius of 7 inches?

Step 1. Substitute $\frac{22}{7}$ for π, and 7 for r in the area formula.
$$A = \frac{22}{7} \times 7 \times 7$$

Step 2. Cancel the first two "7's."
$$A = \frac{22}{{}_1 7} \times 7^1 \times 7$$

Step 3. Multiply 22 by 7.
$$A = 22 \times 7 = 154$$

Answer: **154 square inches**

EXAMPLE 2: What is the area of a circle that has a radius of 2.1 ft.

Step 1. Substitute 3.14 for π, and 2.1 for r in the area formula.
$$A = 3.14 \times 2.1 \times 2.1$$

Step 2. Multiply 2.1 by 2.1.
$$2.1 \times 2.1 = 4.41$$

Step 3. Multiply 3.14 by 4.41.
$$3.14 \times 4.41 = \mathbf{13.8474}$$

Answer: **13.8 square feet**

Note: The answer is rounded off to a single decimal place.

Use the formula $A = \pi r^2$ to find the area of each circle below. **Round off decimal answers to a single decimal place.**

1. A = _____

2. A = _____

3. A = _____

In problems 4, 5, and 6, find the radius ($r = \frac{d}{2}$) as your first step in solving for the area.

4. A = _____
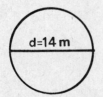

5. A = _____
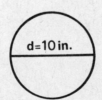

6. A = _____

7. A round glass mirror measures 1 foot from the center to the edge. How many square inches of glass are in the mirror?

_____

8. To the nearest square foot, what is the area of a circular rose garden that measures 28 feet through the center?

_____

9. A sprinkler waters in a circular pattern, spraying water out a distance of 3.1 meters. How much lawn surface does the sprinkler water?

_____

10. If 6 people share a large pizza that has a 14 inch diameter, how much pizza will each person get? Give your answer to the nearest square inch.

_____

11. The circular flat roof of a water tower has a diameter of 28 feet. What is the area of this roof?

_____

12. Radio station KNPA broadcasts its signal to all points within an 84 km radius of the station. What is the area of the region served by this station?

_____

PERIMETER AND AREA: APPLYING YOUR SKILLS

On many tests you may be expected to find the perimeter and area of the four most common figures: square, rectangle, triangle, and circle. The formulas for these figures may not be given on the test.

Below are summarized the six figures we've studied in this chapter. You should memorize how to find the perimeter and area of each of the first four figures. If you do not memorize the formulas for the last two figures, you should be familiar with how to use these formulas when they are given.

TO REMEMBER			
Name	**Example**	**Perimeter**	**Area**
Square		$P = 4s$	$A = s^2$
Rectangle		$P = 2l + 2w$	$A = lw$
Triangle		$P = s_1 + s_2 + s_3$	$A = \frac{1}{2}bh$
Circle		$C = \pi d$ (circumference)	$A = \pi r^2$

Hint: a) To remember perimeters:
   For most figures, remember that perimeter is the sum of the sides.
   For a circle, memorize the circumference formula $C = \pi d$.

   b) To remember areas:
   For most figures, remember to multiply one side by a second side that is perpendicular to the first. For a triangle, this often means multiplying by a height that may not be one of the sides and also remembering to multiply by $\frac{1}{2}$. The $\frac{1}{2}$ is easily remembered because a triangle looks very much like $\frac{1}{2}$ of a rectangle or parallelogram.
   For a circle, memorize the area formula $A = \pi r^2$.

   c) Always remember, the number π is used only with circles.

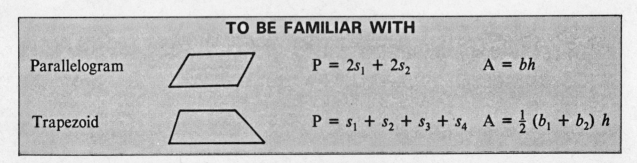

TO BE FAMILIAR WITH			
Parallelogram		$P = 2s_1 + 2s_2$	$A = bh$
Trapezoid		$P = s_1 + s_2 + s_3 + s_4$	$A = \frac{1}{2}(b_1 + b_2)h$

Solve the problems below. Round off decimals to one decimal place.

1. P = _____

    A = _____

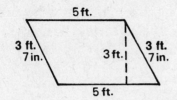

2. P = _____

    A = _____

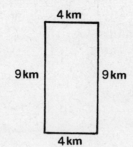

3. P = _____

    A = _____

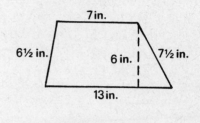

4. P = _____

    A = _____

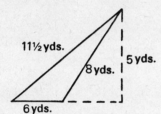

5. C = _____

    A = _____

6. P = _____

    A = _____

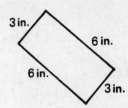

7. C = _____

    A = _____

8. P = _____

    A = _____

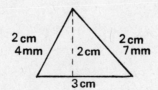

9. P = _____

    A = _____

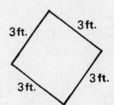

In the following problems, first decide what kind of shape you are working with and whether you are looking for perimeter or area. **Then, solve the problem. Round off decimals to one decimal place.**

10. Bill made a round oak table that he wants to cover with glass. How many square feet of glass are needed if the distance across the center of the table is 4 feet?

_____

11. A swimming pool cover measures 5 meters long by 3 meters wide. At $5.25 per square meter, what is the cost of the cover?

_____

12. After jogging 8 laps around a square field, Anne was curious about how far she had run. What was the total distance she had run if each side of the field measures 105 yards 2 feet?

_____

13. In a carnival ride, the ponies walk in a circle with a 14-foot radius. How far does a child ride if the pony makes ten trips around before the child gets off?

_____

14. The wall of Joan's living room measures 17 feet long and 8 feet high. To buy paint for the room, she needs to know the size of each wall. How large is the living room wall she measured?

_____

15. A rainbird sprinkler sends out water in a circular pattern. If the water reaches out a distance of 3.5 meters from the sprinkler, about how many square meters of lawn does the sprinkler water?

_____

16. Central Park has three sides with lengths of 345 yards 2 feet, 464 yards 1 foot, and 500 yards. How far is it around this park?

_____

17. At the base of Hyde Park is a circular water tower. If the diameter of this tower is 49 feet, what is the distance around it?

_____

18. Marie owns a piece of property with four equal sides. What is the area of this property if each side measures 21 meters?

_____

19. To increase the size of his house, Jim decided to enclose his garage. How much square footage can Jim add to the house if the garage measures 24 feet long by 25 feet wide?

_____

20. Compute how much fence it will take to enclose a triangular garden space which has sides of 12 yards 2 feet, 14 yards 1 foot, and 13 yards 2 feet.

_____

21. To the nearest square foot, how much surface does a wading pool have if the diameter of the circular pool measures 42 feet?

_____

22. The roof on Meg's house consists of two rectangular sides. Each side is 45 feet long and 20 feet wide. What is the total area of roof on Meg's house?

_____

23. Refer to the drawing below. Which of the following fractions results when the area of triangle ABC is divided by the area of the square?

a) $\frac{2}{3}$
b) $\frac{1}{4}$
c) $\frac{1}{3}$
d) $\frac{1}{2}$
e) $\frac{3}{4}$

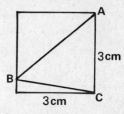

_____

24. Refer to the drawing below. Choose the whole number that is closest to the result of dividing the area of the square by the area of the circle.

a) 4
b) 5
c) 6
d) 7
e) 8

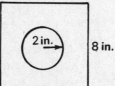

_____

25. George's back yard is in the shape of a trapezoid. What is the distance around the yard if the sides measure 14 m 50 cm, 12 m 80 cm, 15 m 75 cm, and 21 m 25 cm?

_____

SOLVING TWO-STEP AREA PROBLEMS: PART I

Many area problems involve figures that are a combination of common geometrical shapes. We call these problems _two-step area problems_.

To solve a two-step area problem, divide the figure into shapes you are familiar with and then solve for each shape separately.

For example, you may be asked to find the area of the room pictured to the right.

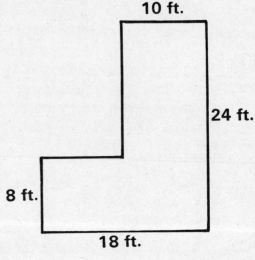

To find this area, follow these steps:

Step 1. Divide the room into 2 rectangles.
Step 2. Find the unknown side of one rectangle.
Step 3. Find the area of each rectangle.
Step 4. Add the areas of the two rectangles.
The example below will show you how to do this.

EXAMPLE: What is the area of the room pictured above?

Step 1. Divide the room into two rectangles. Label the rectangles "I" and "II." Label the unmeasured long side of rectangle I as "_l_" for length. You need to know the value of "_l_" before you can find the area of rectangle I.

Step 2. To find "_l_" subtract 8 from 24.
$$l = 24 - 8$$
$$l = 16$$

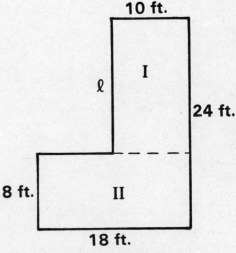

Step 3. Find the area of rectangle I and the area of rectangle II.

Area of I $= lw = 16 \times 10$
$\qquad = 160$ sq. ft.

Area of II $= lw = 18 \times 8$
$\qquad = 144$ sq. ft.

Step 4. Add the areas of rectangles I and II.

$$\begin{array}{r} 160 \text{ sq. ft.} \\ +\underline{144 \text{ sq. ft.}} \\ 304 \text{ sq. ft.} \end{array}$$

The area of the whole is the area of rectangle I plus the area of rectangle II.

Answer: The area of the room is 304 sq. ft.

What is the area of each room pictured below?

1. A = _____

16 ft.

11 ft.   15 ft.

12 ft.

2. A = _____

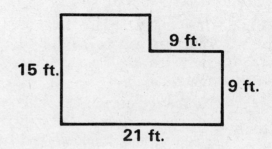

9 ft.

15 ft.   9 ft.

21 ft.

3. A = _____

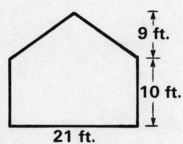

9 ft.

10 ft.

21 ft.

Hint: Problem 3 involves a rectangle and a triangle.

4. A = _____

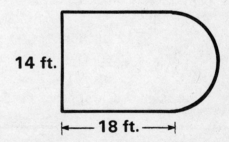

14 ft.

|←— 18 ft. —→|

Hint: Problem 4 involves a rectangle and half of a circle. Do you see a clue for the circle's diameter?

SOLVING TWO-STEP AREA PROBLEMS: PART II

Many area problems require that you subtract a smaller area from a larger area.

EXAMPLE: How many square feet of wallpaper will be needed to cover the wall pictured at right?

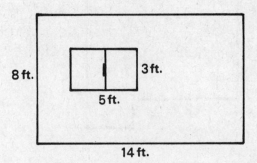

To find the area of the wall, first find the area of the "wall including the window" and then subtract the area of the window.

Step 1. Find the area of the "wall including window."

Area of the "wall including window" = 14 × 8
= 112 sq. ft.

Step 2. Find the area of the window.

Area of window = 5 × 3
= 15 sq. ft.

Step 3. Subtract to find the area of the wall.

112 sq. ft.
−15 sq. ft.
97 sq. ft.

Answer: **The amount of wallpaper needed is 97 square feet.**

Solve the problems below.

1. How many square feet of wallpaper will be needed to cover the wall pictured below?

_____

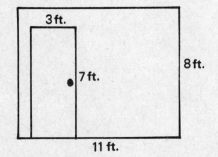

2. How many square feet of tile are needed to cover the patio shown below?

_____

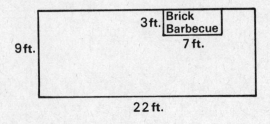

3. Lois's house sits in the middle of her lot. The lot is shaped like a trapezoid. Except for the house and driveway, her lot is covered with grass. How many square feet of grass are on the lot?

_____

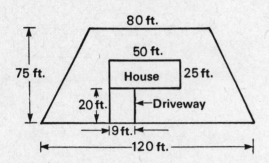

4. The Parks Department wants to put tile around the circular wading pool. How many square feet of tile will be needed?

_____

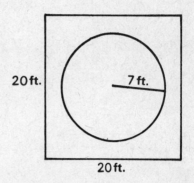

5. Sam, a machinist, wants to cut a circular disc from a square plate of aluminum. From the drawing below, how many square centimeters of surface must be cut away?

_____

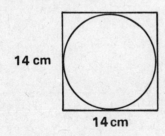

6. Two triangular planters sit in the rose garden. Excluding the planters, how many square feet of garden area remain?

_____

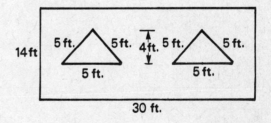

FINAL PLANE FIGURES SKILLS INVENTORY

1. *Add*: 7 yds. 2 ft.
3 yds. 1 ft.
8 yds. 2 ft.

2. *Add*: 9 cm 7 mm
6 cm 8 mm
3 cm 4 mm

3. *Subtract*: 7 ft. 6 in.
3 ft. 9 in.

4. *Subtract*: 35 m 87 cm
14 m 93 cm

5. *Multiply*: 1 m 75 cm
7

6. *Divide*: 6)14 ft. 6 in.

7. *Divide*: 4)5 m 12 cm

8. Marie measured 19 inches on the day she was born. On her fourth birthday, she was 3 feet 5 inches tall. By how much did Marie grow in her first four years?

_____

9. Jesse, a carpenter, wants to cut a 17 foot long board into three equal pieces. To the nearest inch, how long will each piece be?

_____

In problems 10-15, name each of the figures shown.

10. _____

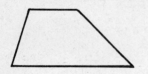

11. _____

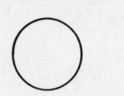

12. _____

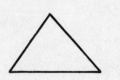

13. _____

14. _____

15. _____

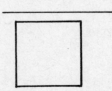

16. Match each formula on the left with the area it represents on the right.

    _____ 1) bh a) area of a square

    _____ 2) $\frac{1}{2}(b_1 + b_2)h$ b) area of a circle

    _____ 3) s^2 c) area of a parallelogram

    _____ 4) $\frac{1}{2}bh$ d) area of a rectangle

    _____ 5) πr^2 e) area of a trapezoid

    _____ 6) lw f) area of a triangle

In problems 17-22, find the perimeter and area of each figure.

17. P = _____

    A = _____

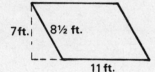

18. P = _____

    A = _____

19. C = _____

    A = _____

20. P = _____

    A = _____

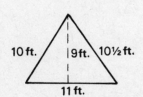

21. P = _____

    A = _____

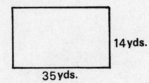

22. P = _____

    A = _____

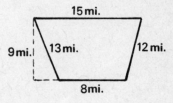

23. Bill wants to put a strip of tile around his circular swimming pool. What is the distance around the pool if the radius of the pool is 7 feet?

_____

24. Find the area of Sally's lot which is in the shape of a square, each side measuring 35 meters?

_____

25. Find the floor area of the recreation room pictured below.

_____

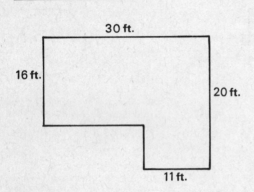

26. How many square feet of paneling will be needed to cover the wall drawn below?

_____

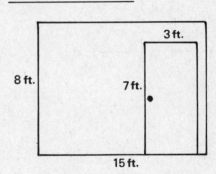

FINAL PLANE FIGURES INVENTORY CHART

Circle the number of any problem that you missed and be sure to review the appropriate page. A passing score is 22 correct answers. If you miss more than four questions, you should review this chapter.

Problem	Skill Area	Page
1	addition: English units	74
2	addition: metric units	74
3	subtraction: English units	74
4	subtraction: metric units	74
5	multiplication: metric units	76
6	division: English units	76
7	division: metric units	76
8	length units: applying skills	78
9	length units: applying skills	78
10	recognizing polygons	82
11	circles	102
12	recognizing polygons	82
13	recognizing polygons	82
14	recognizing polygons	82
15	recognizing polygons	82
16	formulas	106
17	parallelograms: perimeter + area	98
18	squares: perimeter + area	86+88
19	circle: circumference + area	102+104
20	triangles: perimeter + area	94+96
21	rectangles: perimeter + area	90+92
22	trapezoid: perimeter + area	98
23	perimeter + area: applying skills	106
24	perimeter + area: applying skills	106
25	two-step area problems	112
26	two-step area problems	110

SOLID FIGURES

SOLID FIGURES SKILLS INVENTORY

This inventory will let you know what you need to work on in the SOLID FIGURES section of *Number Power: Geometry*.

Do all of the following problems that you can. There is no time limit. Work carefully and check all your answers. On this inventory, you can use the $\frac{22}{7}$ form of π.

---

1. Match each formula on the left with the volume it represents on the right.

1) $\frac{1}{3}\pi r^2 h$ _____   a) volume of a rectangular solid

2) s^3 _____   b) volume of a cylinder

3) lwh _____   c) volume of a cone

4) $\pi r^2 h$ _____   d) volume of a cube

In problems 2–5, find the volume of each figure.

2. V = _____

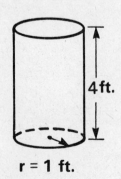

8 in.
7 in.
5 in.

3. V = _____

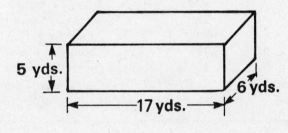

5 yds.
17 yds.
6 yds.

4. V = _____

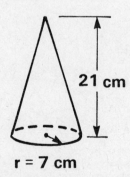

4 ft.
r = 1 ft.

5. V = _____

21 cm
r = 7 cm

6. What is the volume of a room measuring 10 feet on each side?

_____

7. Find the volume of a storage shed that measures 50 meters long, 35 meters wide, and 6 meters high.

_____

8. How many cubic feet of water will a cylindrical storage tank hold if it is 15 feet high and has a radius of 14 feet?

_____

9. A pile of sand is in the shape of a cone. What is the volume of sand that is in a pile measuring 4 yards high and having a diameter of 10 yards?

_____

In problems 10 and 11, find the volume of each figure.

10. V = _____

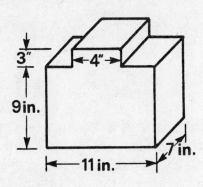

11. V = _____

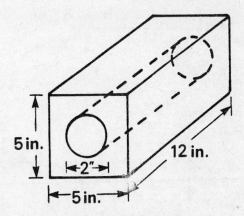

SOLID FIGURES INVENTORY CHART

Use this inventory to see what you already know about solid figures and what you need to work on. A passing score is 8 correct answers. Even if you have a passing score, circle the number of any problem that you miss, correct it, and turn to the practice page indicated.

Problem	Skill Area	Page	Problem	Skill Area	Page
1	formulas	130	7	applying skills	130
2	cube	124	8	applying skills	130
3	rectangular solids	126	9	applying skills	130
4	cylinders	128	10	two-step volume	132
5	cones	129	11	two-step volume	134
6	applying skills	130			

RECOGNIZING COMMON SOLID FIGURES

Solid figures take up space and have volume. Things you can see, touch, and hold are solid figures. There are four shapes of solid figures that occur so frequently that they are of special interest in the study of geometry.

Below are listed the names and descriptions of these common solid figures.

Name	**Example**	**Description**
Cube	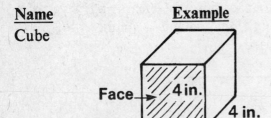	Each side of a *cube* is an equal length, and each pair of sides forms a right angle. Thus, each *face* (flat surface) of a cube is a square.
Rectangular Solid	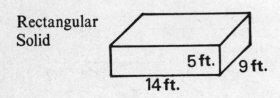	Each face of a *rectangular solid* is either a rectangle or a square. At every corner, each pair of sides forms a right angle.
Cylinder	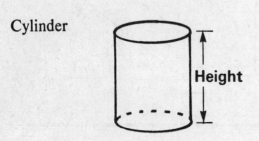	A *cylinder* has the shape of a common tin can. The top and bottom surfaces are circles that are parallel to each other. The distance between the top and bottom is called the *height* of the cylinder.
Cone	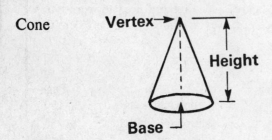	A *cone* has one circular surface called the *base*. The *vertex* of a cone is a point that lies directly above the center of the base. The distance between the vertex and the center of the base is called the *height* of the cone.

Label each figure below with its solid figure name: cube, rectangular solid, cylinder, or cone.

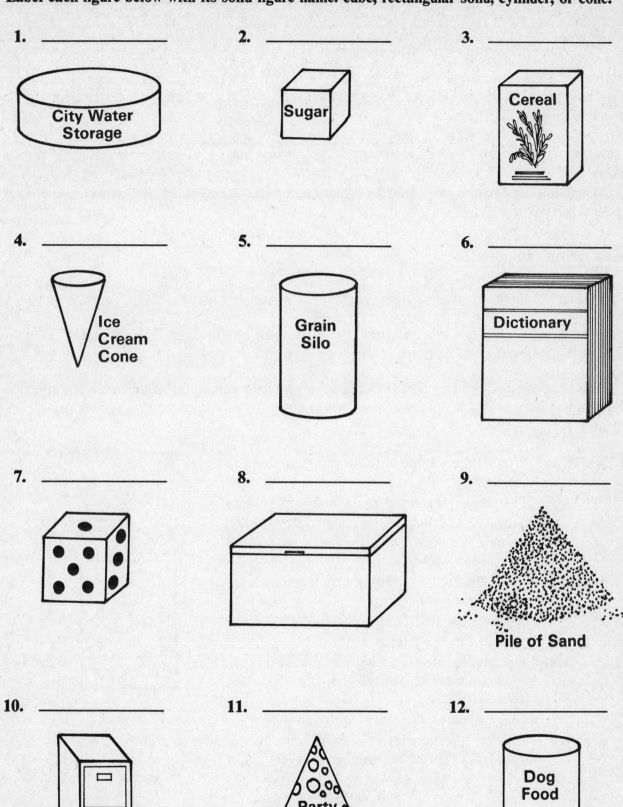

1. _____

City Water Storage

2. _____

Sugar

3. _____

Cereal

4. _____

Ice Cream Cone

5. _____

Grain Silo

6. _____

Dictionary

7. _____

8. _____

9. _____

Pile of Sand

10. _____

11. _____

Party Hat

12. _____

Dog Food

VOLUME

Volume

Volume is a measure of <u>the space *taken up* by a solid figure</u> (or object). A large object has more volume than a small object. For example, the volume of a brick is greater than the volume of a marble.

Volume can also refer to <u>the space *enclosed* by the surface</u> of a solid figure. For example, the volume of a room is the space enclosed by the floor, walls, and ceiling of the room.

Questions on volume may refer to either use of the word volume. In either case, the symbol for volume is "V".

Measuring Volume

To measure volume, we use a <u>*volume unit*</u> in the shape of a cube.

For example, we can use this cube ⬛ as our volume unit. The volume of solid objects is measured in cubic units.

Volume can be found by first dividing an object into volume units and then counting these units.

EXAMPLE: What is the volume of the rectangular solid at the right?

The rectangular solid is divided into volume units. To find the volume, count these units.

Because you can't directly see each volume unit, follow these steps:

Step 1. Count the number of volume units in one layer of the figure.

We have counted (and numbered) 12 volume units in the front layer.

Note: The number of volume units in the front layer is the same as the number of area units on the front surface:

Area of surface = 3 × 4 = 12

Step 2. Multiply the number of volume units in the front layer (12) by the number of layers (3) in the figure.

12 × 3 = **36**

Answer: **V = 36 volume units**

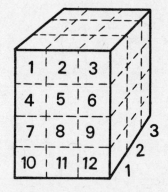

Note: There are 12 volume units in each of 3 layers.

Find the volume of each figure below. Each figure is divided into volume units.

1. V = _____ volume units

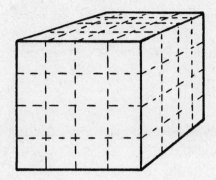

2. V = _____ volume units

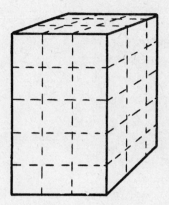

3. V = _____ volume units

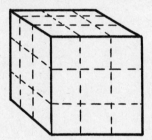

4. V = _____ volume units

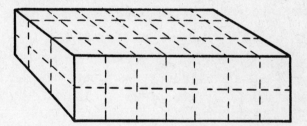

5. V = _____ volume units

6. V = _____ volume units

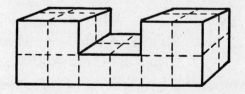

WORKING WITH CUBES

Volume Units

The volume of common geometrical figures is most often found by using a *volume formula*. Using a volume formula is easier than trying to divide a figure into volume units. To use a volume formula, replace letters with numbers and then multiply or divide as indicated. Use the correct volume unit with each answer.

Common volume units include the following:

English Units	Abbreviation
cubic inch	cu. in.
cubic foot	cu. ft.
cubic yard	cu. yd.
cubic mile	cu. mi.

Metric Units	Abbreviation
cubic millimeter	mm^3
cubic centimeter	cm^3
cubic meter	m^3
cubic kilometer	km^3

Volume Of A Cube

The volume of a cube is given by the formula:

$$V = s^3$$

where *s* stands for "side."

Note: s^3 means $s \times s \times s$.

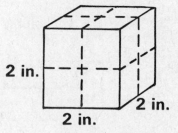

2 in.   2 in.   2 in.

To find the volume of a cube, multiply the value of a side by itself and then multiply this product by the value of the side once more. Try this formula on the cube at the right.

EXAMPLE: What is the volume of the cube pictured at right?

Step 1.   Replace each "*s*" with 4 in the volume formula.

$$V = s^3$$
$$V = 4^3$$

Step 2.   Multiply and solve.

$$V = 4 \times 4 \times 4$$
$$V = 64$$

Since each side is measured in feet, the volume units are written as cubic feet.

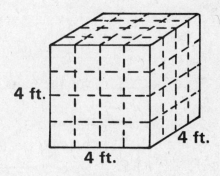

4 ft.   4 ft.   4 ft.

Answer: **The volume is 64 cubic feet.**

Use the formula $V = s^3$ to find the volume of each cube below.

1. V = _____

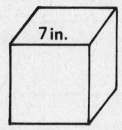

2. V = _____

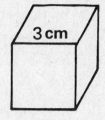

3. V = _____

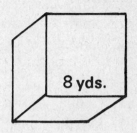

4. A contractor is hired to put "fill dirt" in a hole that is in the shape of a cube. If the hole measures 18 yards on an edge, how much dirt will the contractor need?

   _____

5. Compute the volume of a storage shed that has a square floor 3 meters on each side and is 3 meters high.

   _____

6. A water storage tank in the shape of a cube measures 4.1 meters along each edge. If one cubic meter of water weighs one metric ton, how many metric tons of water can the tank hold?

   _____

7. The Deluxe Calculator Co. packs calculators in cubical shipping boxes that are 2 feet on each side. How many shipping boxes can be put in a moving van that has a packing volume of 896 cubic feet?

   _____

8. Simon's Toy Co. makes plastic blocks that are in the shape of cubes 3 inches on each edge. How many blocks can be put in a cube-shaped mailing box that measures 15 inches on each edge?

   _____

WORKING WITH RECTANGULAR SOLIDS

Volume

The volume of a rectangular solid is given by the formula:

$$V = lwh$$

> where *l* stands for "length"
> *w* stands for "width"
> *h* stands for "height"

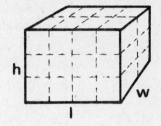

To find the volume of a rectangular solid, multiply the length by the width, and then multiply this product by the height.

EXAMPLE: What is the volume of the rectangular solid at right?

Step 1. Substitute 3 for "*l*," 2 for "*w*," and 4 for "*h*" in the volume formula.

$$V = lwh$$
$$V = 3 \times 2 \times 4$$

Step 2. Multiply and solve.

$$V = 24$$

Write the volume as cubic centimeters.

Answer: **The volume is 24 cm³**

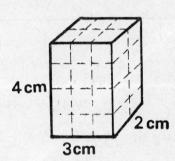

Use the formula **V = *lwh*** to find the volume of the rectangular solids below.

1. V = _____

2. V = _____

3. V = _____

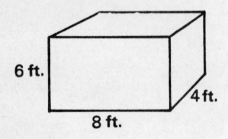

6 ft.

4 ft.

8 ft.

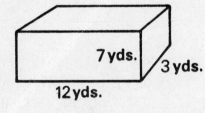

7 yds.

3 yds.

12 yds.

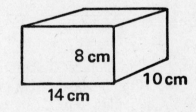

8 cm

10 cm

14 cm

4. V = _____

5. V = _____

6. V = _____

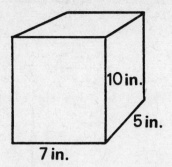

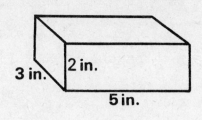

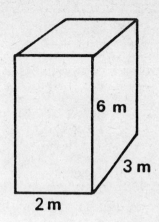

7. How many cubic feet of water are in a water bed that is 6 feet long, 5 feet wide, and $\frac{1}{2}$ foot high?

    _____

8. Find the volume of a storage chest that measures 3 feet long, 2 feet wide, and 2 feet high.

    _____

9. What is the volume of space in a bedroom that measures 4 meters long, 3 meters wide, and $2\frac{1}{2}$ meters high?

    _____

10. A freezer has inside dimensions of 4 feet, 2 feet, and $2\frac{1}{2}$ feet. How many cubic feet of space are inside the freezer?

    _____

WORKING WITH CYLINDERS

Volume

The volume of a cylinder is given by the formula:
$$V = \pi r^2 h$$
where r stands for "radius"
and h stands for "height."

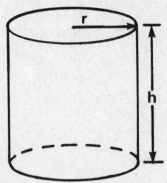

Note: This formula means the volume is equal to π *times* the radius squared *times* the height.

The top and bottom of a cylinder are equal-size circles.

To find the volume of a cylinder, multiply the area of the circular top or bottom (πr^2) times the height.

EXAMPLE: What is the volume of the cylinder at the right?

Step 1. Substitute the values in the problem.
$$V = \pi r^2 h$$
$$V = \tfrac{22}{7} \times 7^2 \times 10$$

Step 2. Find the radius squared.
$$V = \tfrac{22}{7} \times 49 \times 10$$

Step 3. Cancel, if possible. Multiply and solve.
$$V = \tfrac{22}{\cancel{7}^1} \times \cancel{49}^7 \times 10$$
$$V = 1{,}540$$

The volume unit is cubic feet.

Answer: The volume is 1,540 cubic feet.

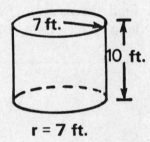

r = 7 ft.

Use the formula $V = \pi r^2 h$ to find the volume of the cylinders below.

1. V = _____

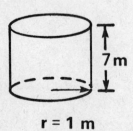

r = 1 m

2. V = _____

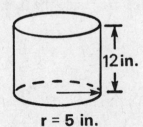

r = 5 in.

3. V = _____

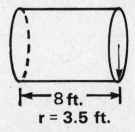

r = 3.5 ft.

WORKING WITH CONES

Volume

The volume of a cone is given by the formula:

$$V = \frac{1}{3} \pi r^2 h$$

where r stands for "radius"
and h stands for "height."

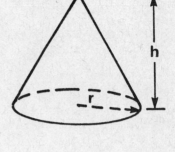

Note: This formula means that the volume of a cone is equal to $\frac{1}{3}$ *times* πr^2 *times* the height.

The volume of a cone is equal to $\frac{1}{3}$ the volume of a cylinder that has the same base area and height.

EXAMPLE: What is the volume of the cone at right?

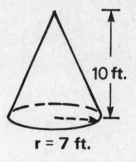

Step 1. Substitute the values.

$$V = \frac{1}{3} \pi r^2 h$$
$$V = \frac{1}{3} \times \frac{22}{7} \times 7^2 \times 10$$

Step 2. Find the radius squared.

$$V = \frac{1}{3} \times \frac{22}{7} \times 49 \times 10$$

Step 3. Cancel, if possible. Multiply and solve.

$$V = \frac{1}{3} \times \frac{22}{\underset{1}{7}} \times \overset{7}{49} \times 10$$

$$V = \frac{22 \times 7 \times 10}{3}$$

$$V = \frac{1{,}540}{3}$$

$$V = 513\frac{1}{3}$$

The volume is in cubic feet.

Answer: The volume is $513\frac{1}{3}$ cubic feet.

Use the formula $V = \frac{1}{3} \pi r^2 h$ to find the volume of the cones below.

1. V = _____

r = 14 ft.

2. V = _____

r = 1 ft.

3. V = _____

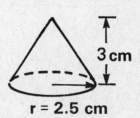

r = 2.5 cm

VOLUME: APPLYING YOUR SKILLS

Learn the figure names and volume formulas as you practice your skills with word problems.

Name	Example	Volume Formula
Cube	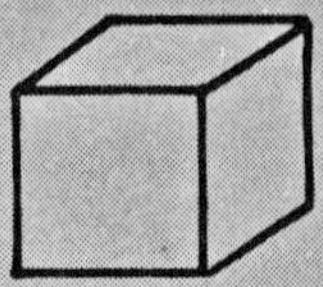	$V = s^3$
Rectangular Solid		$V = lwh$
Cylinder	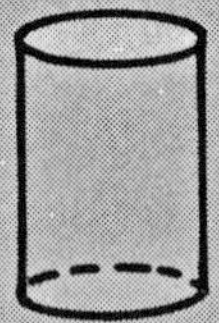	$V = \pi r^2 h$
Cone		$V = \frac{1}{3}\pi r^2 h$

For the problems below, decide which formula is needed and solve.

1. How many cubic feet of concrete will be needed for a driveway section that is 10 feet long, 8 feet wide, and $\frac{1}{2}$ foot thick?

_____

2. A cylindrical water tower is half full of water. How many cubic feet of water are in the tower if it measures 20 feet high and has a radius of 7 feet?

_____

3. A pile of sand is shaped like a cone. If the height of the pile is 7 meters and the radius of the pile is 6 meters, how many cubic meters of sand are in the pile?

_____

4. How many cubic yards of sand will it take to fill a child's play area that measures 10 yards long, 8 yards wide, and $\frac{1}{3}$ yard deep?

_____

5. What is the volume of a storage area measuring 5 feet on each side?

_____

6. A pile of gravel is in the shape of a cone. If the pile is 8 feet high, and the diameter of the pile is 10 feet, how many cubic feet of gravel are in the pile? (_Hint:_ If the diameter is 10, what is the radius?)

_____

7. A cylindrical oil drum is 3 meters high and has a radius of 1 meter. How many cubic meters of oil can the drum hold?

_____

8. How many cubic yards of topsoil are needed to put in a lawn if the lot measures 50 feet by 80 feet and the topsoil is to be $\frac{1}{3}$ foot thick? (_Hint_: As your first step, change all the feet to yards.)

_____

9. What is the volume of a sugar cube that measures 1 cm on each side?

_____

10. A glass is 7 inches high and has a diameter of 3 inches. Approximately how many cubic inches of water can the glass hold when filled to the top?

_____

SOLVING TWO-STEP VOLUME PROBLEMS: PART I

Many volume problems involve figures that combine common geometrical shapes. We call these problems *two-step volume problems*.

To solve a two-step volume problem, divide the figure into shapes with which you are familiar and then find the volume of each part separately.

For example, to find the volume of the figure at the right, follow these steps:

Step 1. Divide the figure into 2 rectangular solids.

Step 2. Find the volume of each rectangular solid.

Step 3. Add the volumes of the two rectangular solids found in Step 2.

The example below illustrates this method.

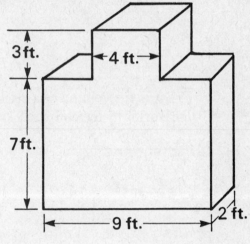

EXAMPLE: What is the volume of the figure pictured at right?

Step 1.   Divide the figure into two rectangular solids. Label these I and II.

Step 2.   Find the volume of each rectangular solid.

Volume of figure I = *lwh*

$$V = 4 \times 2 \times 3$$
$$V = 24 \text{ cubic feet}$$

Volume of figure II = *lwh*

$$V = 9 \times 2 \times 7$$
$$V = 126 \text{ cubic feet}$$

Step 3.   Add the volumes of I and II.

$$
\begin{array}{r}
24 \text{ cubic feet} \\
+126 \text{ cubic feet} \\
\hline
150 \text{ cubic feet}
\end{array}
$$

Answer: The volume of the figure is 150 cubic feet.

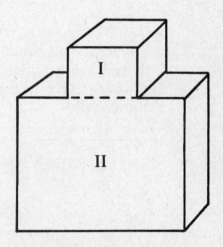

Remember: The volume of the figure is equal to the sum of the volumes of rectangular solids I and II.

1. What is the volume of the figure drawn below?

_____

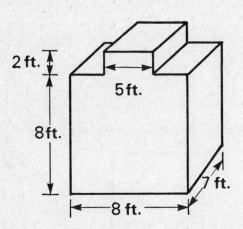

2. How many cubic inches of concrete are needed for the section of curb shown below?

_____

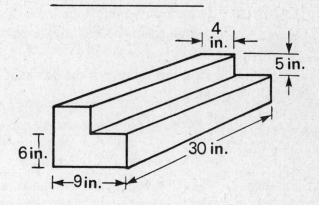

3. What is the volume of the mailbox shown below? (*Hint:* The mailbox can be thought of as a half-cylinder plus a rectangular solid.)

_____

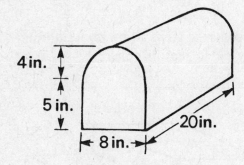

4. What is the volume of the figure below? (*Hint:* The figure can be separated into a cylinder and a cone.)

_____

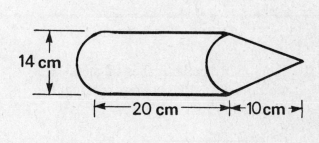

SOLVING TWO-STEP VOLUME PROBLEMS: PART II

Many volume problems are solved by subtracting a smaller volume from a larger volume.

EXAMPLE: How many cubic inches of metal are contained in the rectangular bar at the right?

Step 1. Find the volume of the bar as if it were solid.

Volume of solid bar = lwh

$= 8 \times 4 \times 4$

$= 128$ cubic inches

Step 2. Find the volume of the space taken by the hole drilled through the bar.

Volume of hole in bar = $\pi r^2 h$

$= \frac{22}{7} \times 1 \times 1 \times 8$

$= \frac{176}{7}$

$= 25\frac{1}{7}$ cubic inches

Step 3. Subtract to find the volume of the metal in the bar. Write 128 as $127\frac{7}{7}$.

$128\frac{7}{7}$ cubic inches

$-25\frac{1}{7}$ cubic inches

$102\frac{6}{7}$ cubic inches

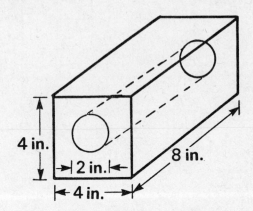

Note: The amount of metal in the bar is equal to the volume of the rectangular solid minus the volume of the cylindrical hole that has a radius of 1 inch.

Answer: The amount of metal left in the bar is $102\frac{6}{7}$ cubic inches.

---

1. How many cubic inches of metal are contained in the hollow rectangular tube below?

2. The concrete steps below contain how many cubic feet of concrete?

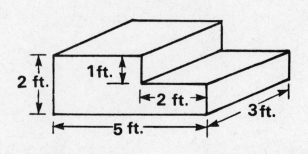

3. What is the volume of the slotted beam below?

_____

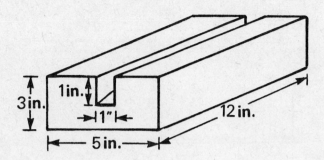

4. How many cubic inches of metal are contained in the rectangular bar below?

_____

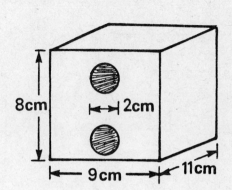

5. Find the volume of the hollow tube shown below.

_____

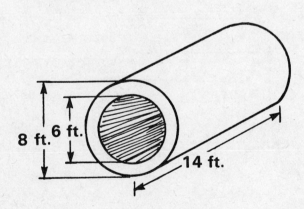

6. How many cubic inches of metal are contained in the cylinder drawn below?

_____

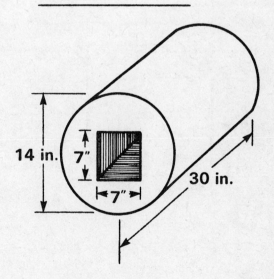

FINAL SOLID FIGURES SKILLS INVENTORY

In problems 1-3, name each figure shown.

1. _____   2. _____   3. _____

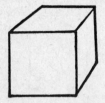      

4. Match each formula on the left with the volume it represents on the right.

1) lwh _____   a) volume of a cylinder

2) $\pi r^2 h$ _____   b) volume of a cube

3) $\frac{1}{3}\pi r^2 h$ _____   c) volume of a rectangular solid

4) s^3 _____   d) volume of a cone

In problems 5-8, find the volume of each figure shown. You may use the $\frac{22}{7}$ form of π.

5. V = _____   6. V = _____

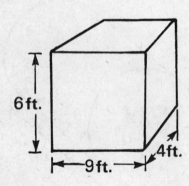   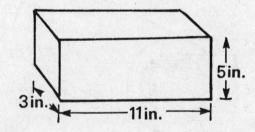

7. V = _____

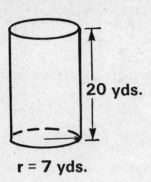

20 yds.

r = 7 yds.

8. V = _____

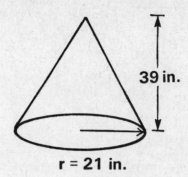

39 in.

r = 21 in.

9. How many cubic yards of dirt will it take to fill a hole that is in the shape of a cube 3 yards on each side?

_____

10. Decide how many cubic feet of space are in a moving van that is shaped like a rectangular solid and has the following dimensions: length = 20 feet, width = 7 feet, and height = 8 feet.

_____

11. A cylindrical grain silo is 100 feet high and has a radius of 14 feet. How many cubic feet of grain can be kept in the silo?

_____

12. A pile of gravel is in the shape of a cone. How many cubic yards of gravel are contained in a pile 10 yards high and 14 yards in diameter?

_____

In problems 13-14, find the volume of each figure. You may use the $\frac{22}{7}$ form of π.

13. V = _____

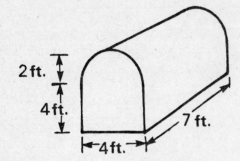

2 ft.

4 ft.

7 ft.

4 ft.

14. V = _____

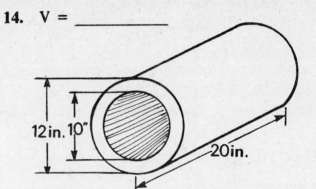

12 in. 10"

20 in.

FINAL SOLID FIGURES INVENTORY CHART

Circle the number of any problem that you missed and be sure to review the appropriate page. A passing score is 11 correct answers. If you miss more than three questions, you should review this chapter.

Problem	Skill Area	Page
1	solid figures	120
2	solid figures	120
3	solid figures	120
4	formulas	130
5	cubes	124
6	rectangular solids	126
7	cylinders	128
8	cones	129
9	applying skills	130
10	applying skills	130
11	applying skills	130
12	applying skills	130
13	two-step volume	132
14	two-step volume	134

REVIEW TEST

BUILDING NUMBER POWER: GEOMETRY REVIEW TEST

This review gives you a chance to check your skills in applying geometry to the type of questions asked on the GED and other tests. Take your time and work each problem carefully. When you finish, check your answers and review any topics on which you need more work.

1. How many degrees are in one-fourth of a circle?

    _____

2. As shown at the right, a pie is cut into eight equal pieces. At what acute angle is each piece cut?

    _____

Problems 3 and 4 refer to the drawing at the right.

3. If Harlow Road intersects I-5 at a right angle, at what acute angle does Harlow Road intersect I-40?

    _____

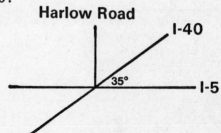

4. What is the value of the obtuse angle that I-5 makes with I-40?

    _____

Problems 5 and 6 refer to the drawing at the right.

5. At what acute angle does the Amtrak line cross Madison Street?

_____

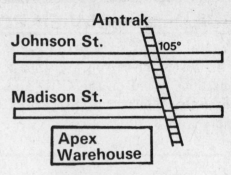

6. What is the value of the obtuse angle that the Amtrak line makes with Madison Street near the Apex Warehouse?

_____

Note: Johnson St. is parallel to Madison St.

7. What is the roof angle (angle *b*) in the drawing at the right?

_____

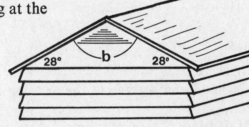

8. In triangle ABC, $\angle A = 34°$ and $\angle B = 47°$. What is the value of $\angle C$?

_____

9. A surveyor wants to find the distance across Yellowstone River at Forest Camp. Use the drawing at the right that she made to determine this distance.

_____

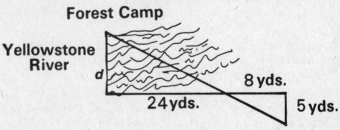

10. At 2:00 p.m., a 6-foot tall man cast an 8-foot shadow. If, at the same time, a nearby tree cast a 100-foot shadow, how high is the tree?

_____

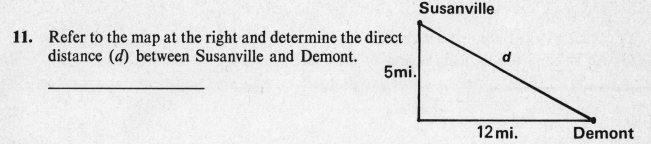

11. Refer to the map at the right and determine the direct distance (*d*) between Susanville and Demont.

_____

12. One side of a right triangle measures 6 meters. If the hypotenuse measures 10 meters, what is the length of the third side?

_____

13. Bill bought 100 feet of fencing material to enclose his rectangular garden. Subtracting 3 feet for a gate, how much material will he have left over if his garden measures 27 feet 9 inches by 19 feet 5 inches?

_____

14. How many square yards of carpet are needed to carpet a rectangular room that measures 4 yards by 5 yards?

_____

15. What is the area of the triangle drawn at the right?

_____

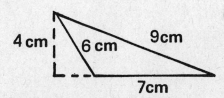

16. Which of the formulas at the right represents the area of a circle?

a) $\frac{1}{2}bh$
b) πr^2
c) $4s$
d) πd
e) $2l + 2w$

_____

17. Using the area formula for a trapezoid, $A = \frac{1}{2}(b_1 + b_2)h$, find the area of the figure below.

_____

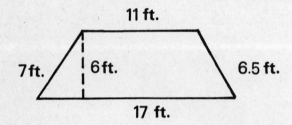

11 ft.

7 ft.   6 ft.   6.5 ft.

17 ft.

18. Refer to the drawing below. Which of the following fractions is equivalent to the fraction formed by dividing the area of the circle by the area of the square? (Use $\frac{22}{7}$ for π.)

_____

a) $\frac{22}{14}$
b) $\frac{14}{17}$
c) $\frac{28}{13}$
d) $\frac{11}{14}$
e) $\frac{22}{25}$

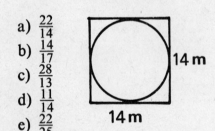

14 m

14 m

19. Bill's house sits in the middle of his lot which is in the shape of a rectangle. Except for the driveway and the house, the lot is planted in grass. As shown below, how many square feet of the lot is planted in grass?

_____

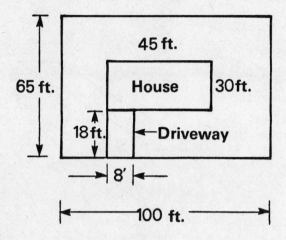

20. What is the storage volume of a cabinet that has inside dimensions of 7 feet high by 4 feet wide by $2\frac{1}{2}$ feet deep?

_____

21. Which of the formulas at the right represents the volume of a cylinder?

_____

a) lwh
b) πr^2
c) $\frac{1}{3} \pi r^2 h$
d) s^3
e) $\pi r^2 h$

22. Use the volume formula for a cone, $V = \frac{1}{3} \pi r^2 h$, to find the volume of the pile of gravel shown at the right.

_____

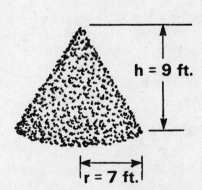

23. A contractor is pouring 12-foot long sections of curb as shown at the right. How many 12-foot sections of curb can he pour for each 108 cubic feet of concrete he mixes?

_____

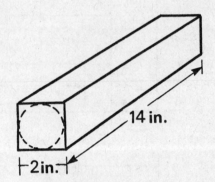

½ ft.

½ ft.

12 ft.

1ft.

1½ft.

24. A machinist "turns" a square rod and makes a cylindrical bar. As shown at the right, the diameter of the finished cylindrical bar equals the width of the uncut rod. For a 14″ length of rod, how much metal is removed to make this bar round?

_____

14 in.

2 in.

The diameter of the finished bar is equal to the width of the uncut rod.

GEOMETRY REVIEW TEST INVENTORY CHART

Circle the number of any problem that you miss and be sure to review the appropriate practice page. A passing score is 19 correct answers.

Problem	Skill Area	Page	Problem	Skill Area	Page
1	measurement of angles	8	13	rectangle: perimeter	90
2	measurement of angles	8	14	rectangle: area	96
3	complementary angles	18	15	triangle: area	96
4	supplementary angles	18	16	circle: area	104
5	parallel lines cut by transversal	23	17	trapezoid: area	100
6	parallel lines cut by transversal	23	18	applying skills	106
7	sum of angles: applying skills	38	19	two-step area problems	112
8	triangles: sum of angles	36	20	rectangular solids	126
9	similar triangles: applying skills	53	21	cylinder	128
10	similar triangles: applying skills	53	22	cones	129
11	Pythagorean Theorem: applying skills	60	23	two-step volume problems	132
12	Pythagorean Theorem: applying skills	60	24	two-step volume problems	134

Review any remaining problem areas. If you passed the test, go on to Using Number Power. If you did not pass the test, take the time to make a more thorough review of the book.

USING NUMBER POWER

THE WORK TRIANGLE

Probably no room in your house is used more than your kitchen. In fact, the kitchen is such an important room that studies have been done to identify what the characteristics of an ideal kitchen might be.

Home economists have noted that the kitchen can be divided into three main work areas: the sink, the stove, and the refrigerator. The most practical and efficient kitchen is one in which these three work areas are placed so that they form the vertex points of a triangle. This triangle is often called the *work triangle.*

Ideally, the distances between work areas should be as follows:

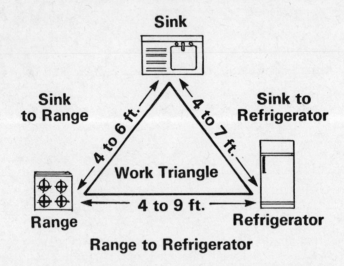

Note: Work areas should not be closer together than 4 feet.

The perimeter of the work triangle is a measure of kitchen efficiency. For a very efficient kitchen, this perimeter should be no more than 22 feet. Also, for a person working alone in the kitchen, the most efficient work triangle is an equilateral triangle with each side measuring 4 feet.

1. a) What is the perimeter of the work triangle of the kitchen pictured at the right?

_____

b) Would you say this is a kitchen correctly designed for work efficiency?

_____

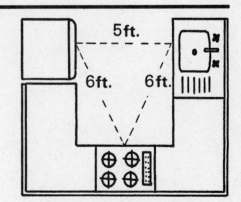

The work triangle (dotted line) joins the front centers of the refrigerator, range, and sink.

2. a) What is the perimeter of the work triangle of the kitchen at right?

_____

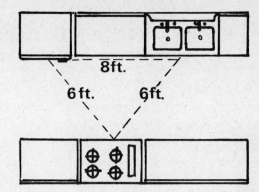

b) Compare the perimeters of the work triangles to decide if this kitchen is as efficiently designed as the kitchen in problem #1.

_____

3. In the kitchen at the right, the refrigerator can be placed at either point A or point B. Which location gives the greatest work efficiency? Why?

_____

_____

_____

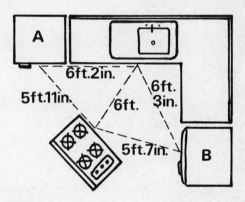

4. Use the work triangle idea to design an ideal kitchen for one person.

a) The ideal kitchen is drawn in the shape of what kind of triangle?

_____

b) What is the length of each side of the work triangle?

_____

Draw the kitchen here.

APPLYING THE PYTHAGOREAN THEOREM

The _Pythagorean Theorem_ is often used to find long distances. To use this theorem to solve the problems in this section, you need to know how to find or to approximate the square root of large numbers. Often, this is easily done by using a hand calculator. Another way is to write a table of perfect squares and approximate the square root you need to the nearest whole number.

For the problems below, use the Partial Table of Perfect Squares at right to approximate the square roots needed to solve each problem.

The symbol "$\approx$" stands for "is approximately equal to." Approximate the square root by finding the closest number on the table at right.

Partial Table of Perfect Squares	
$\vdots$	$\vdots$
$24^2 = 576$	$71^2 = 5{,}041$
$25^2 = 625$	$72^2 = 5{,}184$
$26^2 = 676$	$73^2 = 5{,}329$
$\vdots$	$\vdots$
$44^2 = 1{,}936$	$100^2 = 10{,}000$
$45^2 = 2{,}025$	$101^2 = 10{,}201$
$46^2 = 2{,}116$	$102^2 = 10{,}404$
$\vdots$	$\vdots$

Find the approximate square root in each of the following problems. The first has been done as an example.

1. A power company employee is going to run a power line from the power pole to the back of Joel's house. Use the drawing at the right, and determine the approximate length of cable the employee will need.
    $$c^2 = a^2 + b^2$$
    $$c^2 = 64^2 + 77^2$$
    $$c^2 = 4{,}096 + 5{,}929$$
    $$c^2 = 10{,}025$$
    $$c = \sqrt{10{,}025}$$
    Since 10,025 is closest to 10,000 on the table above, the approximate square root of 10,025 is 100.
    $$c \approx 100 \text{ ft.}$$

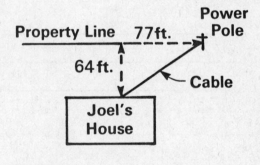

2. A forest ranger at Oak Ridge Lookout spotted a fire 24 miles west of his location. If the town of Olene is 38 miles due south, how far is Olene from the fire?

    _____ _____

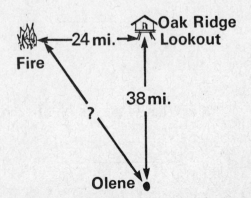

3. A disabled ship radios to shore for help. The Coast Guard determines that the ship is 16 miles east and 43 miles north of the station. What is the direct distance between the ship and the Coast Guard station?

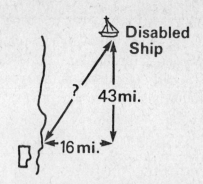

_____

4. Bill Adamly wants to hike directly from Mt. Scott to Mt. St. Clair. In mountain terrain, he can average about one mile for each hour he hikes. Use the map at the right to estimate how long it will take Bill to hike between the two mountains.

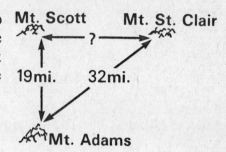

_____

5. Jackson is 54 miles from Lazy R Resort. Ontario is 31 miles south of Jackson. A land developer proposes building a shortcut road to directly connect Ontario and Lazy R. Use his drawing at the right to estimate the length of this new road.

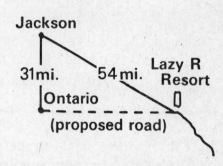

_____

6. Radio station KNPG in Bingham has a broadcast range of 70 miles. Refer to the drawing at the right and determine if Ellensburg is within the broadcast range of KNPG.

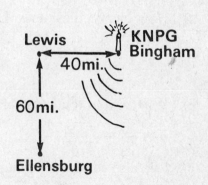

_____

7. Eva Lewis wants to put an underground sprinkler system in her back yard. A drawing of the system is shown at the right. About how many feet of water pipe will Eva need? (_Hint:_ The unmeasured length of pipe is equal to the hypotenuse of a right triangle.)

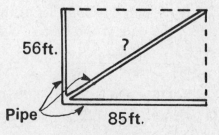

_____

TILING A ROOM

Tiling a room is a home-improvement activity that many people do themselves. No particular professional skills are needed, and tiles can be laid in a short time.

There are three main types of tile available. Although costs vary with location, the following are average prices:

Type of Tile	Cost per Tile	Size of Tile	Use of Tile
Self-stick vinyl	$ .65 to $1.50	12″ by 12″ square	Use over old tile or linoleum.
Vinyl-asbestos*	$ .25 to $1.00	12″ by 12″ square	Use on new (particle-board or concrete) floor where average wear is expected.
Asphalt*	about $ .70	9″ by 9″ square	Use on floor where very tough wear is expected.

* Mastic (tile glue) is required. Mastic costs about $6.00 a quart (to cover 40 sq. ft.).

Follow these steps to compute the cost of tiling a room:

1) Find the floor area to be tiled.
2) Find the number of tiles needed by dividing the floor area by the area of each tile.
3) Multiply the number of tiles needed by the cost per tile.
4) Add the cost of mastic if it is needed.

---

1. Lila Andrews wants to tile the living room shown at the right. She chooses self-stick vinyl tile that costs $ .80 for each 12″ by 12″ (1 sq. ft.) tile.

a) How many tiles does Lila need for the living room?

_____

b) What is the total cost of this tile?

_____

c) Lila also considers buying tile at a "close-out" sale for $ .50 per 12″ by 12″ tile. However, she would have to buy 350 tiles at this price. What would be the cost of these 350 "close-out" tiles?

_____

d) How many "close-out" tiles would Lila have left over after tiling the living room?

_____

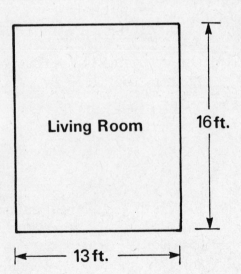

Living Room — 16 ft. — 13 ft.

2. Lila also decides to tile the family room shown at the right. She buys tiles at a "close-out sale" for $.50 per 12″ by 12″ tile. However, to buy the tile at this low price, she has to buy 250 tiles.

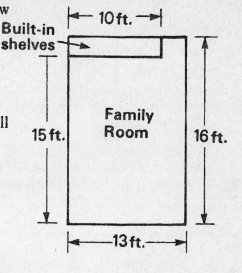

a) What is the total cost of the tile?

———————————

b) After tiling the family room, how many tiles will Lila have left over?
Note: There are no tiles under the shelves.

———————————

3. George Lawson plans to put asphalt tile on his shop floor. The tile he's chosen costs $.75 per 9″ by 9″ tile.

a) What is the area of the shop floor to be tiled? The cabinet area is not tiled.

———————————

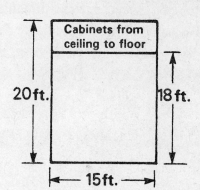

b) How many 9″ by 9″ tiles are needed? (Round off to nearest whole number.)
Hint: Since 9″ = $\frac{3}{4}$ ft., a tile that is
9″ by 9″ is $\frac{3}{4} \times \frac{3}{4} = \frac{9}{16}$ sq. ft.

———————————

c) What is the total cost of tiles?

———————————

Note: Mastic is applied to the floor before asphalt tile is laid.

d) If each quart can of mastic covers about 40 sq. ft., how many cans of mastic are required?

———————————

e) What is the total cost of the mastic?

———————————

f) What is the total cost of the tiles plus the mastic?

———————————

BUILDING A PATIO

Although it requires some work, many people build their own patio. In doing so, they save about half the cost of having a patio built for them.

A simply built patio can be made from a 4-inch thick slab of concrete. You first make "forms" out of two-by-fours to contain the wet concrete, and then you have ready-to-pour concrete delivered and poured directly into the forms. As the concrete is poured, you smooth it out to fill the forms.

The cost of delivered ready-to-pour concrete (often called "mud") varies with location, but an average price is about $70.00 per cubic yard. To find the cost of building your own concrete patio, multiply the number of cubic yards of concrete needed by the price of concrete per cubic yard.

1. Determine the cost of concrete required for the patio at right by answering the following questions.

   a) What are the dimensions of the patio in yards?
      (*Hint:* To change feet to yards, divide by 3. To change inches to yards, divide by 36.)

      Length = 21 ft. = _____ yds.
      Width = 15 ft. = _____ yds.
      Thickness = 4 in. = _____ yds.

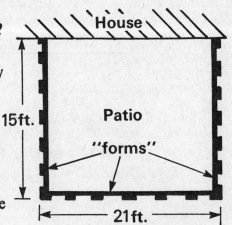

   b) What is the volume, in cubic yards, of concrete needed for the patio?

      _____

   c) Paying $72.00 per cubic yard, what is the cost of the concrete?

      _____

   d) What would be the additional cost of covering the finished patio with a ceramic tile that costs $1.50 per square foot?

      _____

A concrete patio is made by pouring a 4-inch thick layer of concrete on level ground. The drying concrete is held in place by "forms" made of two-by-fours placed around the perimeter of the patio. These forms are removed when the concrete has hardened.

2. George is saving $40.00 a month to pay for a patio he wants to build himself. A drawing of the patio is at the right.

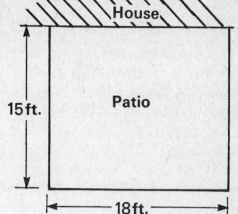

a) How many cubic yards of concrete will be needed for this 4″ thick patio?

_____

b) At $69.00 per cubic yard, how much will the concrete cost?

_____

c) How many months must George save to have enough money to pay for the concrete?

_____

3. Janet is building herself a patio as shown at the right. The patio is in the shape of a half-circle and is 4 inches thick. (In these problems, use the decimal form of π—3.14.)

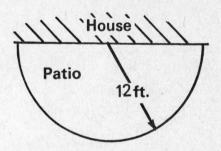

a) To the nearest cubic yard, how much concrete will Janet need for her patio?

_____

b) At $72.00 per cubic yard, what will she pay for this concrete?

_____

c) Janet also wants to put a fancy brick edge along the circular perimeter of the patio. If each brick is 1 foot long, about how many bricks will she need?

_____

d) At $.79 per brick, how much will she pay for the brick perimeter?

_____

CARPETING A ROOM

Carpet is sold by the square yard. The price usually includes the cost of installation and the cost of a carpet pad, a foam rubber pad that is put on the floor under the carpet.

Cutting a carpet to fit a room and installing the carpet require professional skills and tools. Because of this, the cutting and installing of carpet is usually done by personnel from the store where you purchase your carpet.

When you buy carpet, you usually have to buy a piece that is larger than the room you are carpeting. This is because carpet comes in a 12-foot wide roll. You can have it cut to any length you want, but you usually must buy a 12-foot wide piece.

To find the cost of carpeting a room, multiply the number of square yards of carpet to be purchased times the price per square yard.

---

1. Figure out the cost of carpeting the bedroom at the right by answering the following questions.

   a) What are the dimensions of the room in yards? (*Hint:* To change feet to yards, divide by 3.)
   Length = 13 ft. = _____ yds.
   Width = 12 ft. = _____ yds.

   _____

   b) What is the area, in square yards, of carpet needed for this room?

   _____

   c) At $15.00 per square yard for carpet, pad, and installation, what is the cost of carpeting this bedroom?

   _____

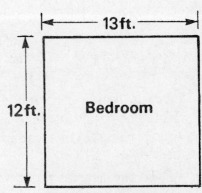

Because the bedroom is 12 ft. wide, a piece of carpet can be purchased that is the same size as the room.

2. How much will Mary pay to have her daughter's room carpeted if she pays $15.75 per square yard for carpet, pad, and installation?

   _____

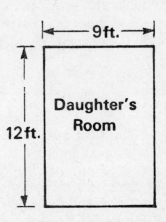

3. To carpet the dining room at the right, Charles must buy a piece of carpet that is larger than the room itself. Refer to the drawing and answer these questions:

a) How many square yards of carpet must Charles buy to carpet the room?

_____

b) At $14.00 per square yard for carpet, pad, and installation, what is the cost of carpeting this room?

_____

c) How many square feet of carpet will Charles have left over?

_____

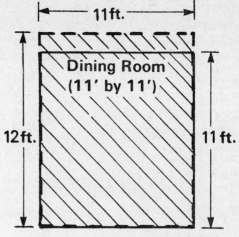

Size of carpet purchased.

Note: Because carpet can only be purchased in a 12-foot width, a piece 11 ft. by 12 ft. must be purchased to carpet a room that measures 11 ft. by 11 ft. The carpet is cut to fit the room, and the "leftover" piece belongs to the buyer.

4. a) What is the cost of carpeting the dining room at the right if the cost of carpet, pad, and installation is $18.00 per square yard?

_____

b) How many square feet of carpet will be left over?

_____

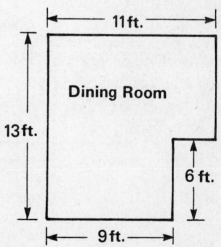

YARD WORK

Lucy Boyd plans to make some improvements in her back yard. She wants to put a circular rose garden in the back yard and a vegetable garden behind the yard. She also plans to put a picket fence around the rose garden and a cedar fence around the vegetable garden. To enrich the grass, she is going to use lawn fertilizer.

To help estimate costs, she drew the following picture of her back yard.

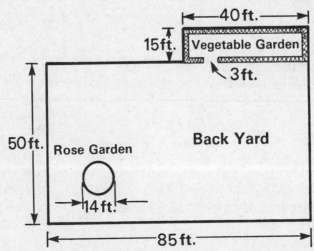

Using the drawing above, answer the following questions to help estimate the costs of Lucy's yard improvement ideas.

Lawn Costs

1. Lucy plans to fertilize the lawn. Lawn fertilizer costs $3.80 a bag, and each bag holds enough fertilizer to cover about 1,500 square feet of lawn.

   a) Not counting the rose and vegetable gardens, what is the area of backyard lawn that Lucy needs to fertilize?

   _____

   b) If Lucy also has 4,600 square feet in her front and side lawns, how many bags of fertilizer will she need for the entire lawn?

   _____

   c) What will be the total cost of fertilizer?

   _____

Rose Garden Costs

2. Lucy wants to plant individual rosebushes in her garden. The salesperson tells her that for the variety of rose she wants, she should allow about 14 square feet of garden space for each plant.

   a) About how many rosebushes can Lucy plant in her circular rose garden?

   _____

   b) If each rosebush costs $6.95, what will be the total cost of the rosebushes?

   _____

   c) The decorative picket fence she's chosen comes in 1-foot sections. At $0.89 per 1-foot section, what will be the total cost of picket fence material?

   _____

Vegetable Garden Costs

3. Because her soil quality is poor, Lucy decides to add a 4-inch layer of organic topsoil to her vegetable garden.

   a) What is the area of the vegetable garden space?

   _____

   b) At $22 per cubic yard, what will be the total cost of topsoil? (*Hint:* When spread to a depth of 4 inches, 1 cubic yard of topsoil will cover about 80 **square** feet of garden space.)

   _____

   c) Lucy also wants to fence the vegetable garden. The fence will enclose the garden except for a 3-foot gate. At $1.29 per foot, approximately how much will the cedar fence material cost Lucy?

   _____

CHANGING VOLUME TO CAPACITY

In our study of geometry, we have referred to the space taken up by an object as its volume. When you measure the amount of liquid that a container will hold, you give that volume the special name, _capacity_. In the English System, familiar units of capacity are the cup, pint, quart, and gallon. In the metric system, they are the liter and milliliter. Capacity units are directly related to the common volume units we have been using.

In many occupations, it is necessary to measure the volume of space inside an object and then to convert this measurement to capacity units. On these two pages, we'll look at the most common example: converting cubic feet to gallons.

For the example and the problems, you need to know that 1 cubic foot = $7\frac{1}{2}$ gallons.

EXAMPLE: How many gallons of water will the container drawn at the right hold?

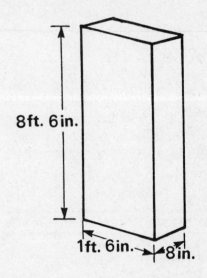

Step 1. Change each distance to feet only.

length: 1' 6" = $1\frac{1}{2}$ ft.

width: 8" = $\frac{2}{3}$ ft.

height: 8' 6" = $8\frac{1}{2}$ ft.

Step 2. Find the volume in cubic feet by multiplying length times width times height. To multiply, express each distance as an improper fraction.

$V = lwh$

$V = 1\frac{1}{2} \times \frac{2}{3} \times 8\frac{1}{2}$

$V = \frac{1\cancel{3}}{1\cancel{2}} \times \frac{\cancel{2}^1}{\cancel{3}_1} \times \frac{17}{2} = \frac{17}{2}$ or $8\frac{1}{2}$ cubic feet

Step 3. To find the number of gallons in the container, multiply the number of cubic feet $(8\frac{1}{2})$ by the number of gallons in each cubic foot $(7\frac{1}{2})$.

Number of gallons = $8\frac{1}{2} \times 7\frac{1}{2}$

$= \frac{17}{2} \times \frac{15}{2} = \frac{255}{4} = 63\frac{3}{4}$

Answer: **The container will hold $63\frac{3}{4}$ gallons of water.**

1. Arny works in a sheet metal shop and makes custom built containers. He has an order for a custom built gasoline tank as shown at right. How many gallons of gas will this tank hold?

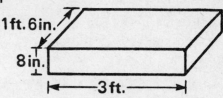

_____

2. Dave's Auto Shop specializes in engine tune-up. Dave averages 7 oil changes a day, and he stores the used oil in the barrel shown at the right. If an oil change averages 1 gallon of used oil, how many days does it take Dave to fill the storage barrel?

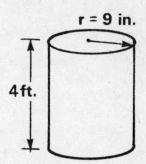

_____

3. A waterbed mattress is shown at the right. To determine the weight of this mattress when it is full of water, answer these questions.

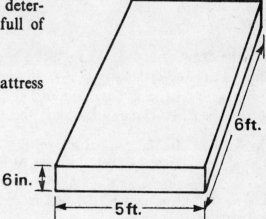

a) How many cubic feet of water does the mattress hold when full?

_____

b) How many gallons of water is this?

_____

c) If water weighs about $8\frac{1}{3}$ pounds per gallon, what is the weight of water in the full waterbed?

_____

4. Dorothy wants to design a water tank that will hold at least 100 gallons of water. Does the tank she designed, shown at the right, meet her requirement?

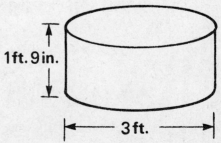

_____

USING GEOMETRY IN PHOTOGRAPHY

Photography is the process of recording an image on film placed inside a camera. "Prints" (commonly called "pictures") are then made from the image that appears on the processed film—called a "negative."

An image is produced on film when light from the subject being photographed passes through a lens and exposes the film. Using geometry and a simple camera, we can understand the relation between the height of the subject and the height of the image.

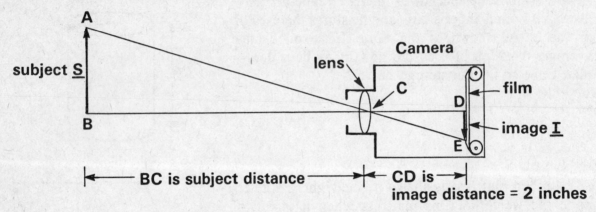

In the drawing above, the subject S is being photographed. The image I appears on the film. The image distance CD is commonly called the *focal length*.

Triangles ABC and CDE are similar triangles and are formed by rays of light moving from the subject, through the lens, and to the film.

EXAMPLE: In the camera above, the image distance (focal length CD) is 2 inches. What is the height of the image on the film if the subject is a 50 foot high tree that is 200 feet from the camera?

Step 1. Convert all distances to inches.
AB = 50 feet = 50 × 12 = 600 inches
CD = 2 inches
BC = 200 feet = 200 × 12 = 2,400 inches

Step 2. Write a proportion.
$$\frac{\text{image height}}{\text{subject height}} = \frac{\text{image distance}}{\text{subject distance}}, \text{ or } \frac{DE}{AB} = \frac{CD}{BC}$$
where DE = I, the image height you are trying to find.
Thus, $\frac{I}{600} = \frac{2}{2,400}$

Step 3. Solve for I.
a) Cross-multiply.   2,400 × I = 2 × 600
                                    2,400 I = 1,200
b) To find I, divide $I = \frac{1,200}{2,400} = \frac{1}{2}$
1,200 by 2,400.

Answer: The size of the image on the film is $\frac{1}{2}$ inch.

Use the proportion $\frac{\text{image height}}{\text{subject height}} = \frac{\text{image distance}}{\text{subject distance}}$ to solve each problem below.

1. Using a camera with a 1 inch focal length (image distance), what is the height of the image when the subject is a 200 foot high building that is 500 feet away?

   _____

2. Sarah uses a 35 mm camera that has a focal length of 2 inches. For this camera, the maximum image height is 1 inch.

   a) If Sarah photographs her 5 foot tall sister, how far should Sarah stand from her so that the image will be the maximum 1 inch?

   _____

   b) What will be the height of the image if Sarah stands 25 feet from her sister?

   _____

3. Using a "zoom lens," a photographer can change the focal length over a wide range of values. A zoom lens allows you to change the image size without changing your distance from the subject.

   a) If you wish to photograph a 125-foot-high tree from the other side of a 875-foot-wide canyon, what focal length is needed to produce a 1 inch high image?

   _____

   b) Taking a picture at this same distance, what would be the size of the image if you changed the focal length to 5 inches?

   _____

GEOMETRIC ILLUSIONS

In your study of geometry, you have learned about the measurement of angles, length, area, and volume. Another interesting topic in geometry is _geometric illusions._

A geometric illusion is produced when one or more geometric figures appears distorted or different than it really is due to the presence of other figures. You'll never be tested on your knowledge of geometric illusions, but they are fun to look at. We will show you several well-known illusions on these next two pages.

Line-length Illusions

In each drawing below, which line in each pair looks longer? Use a ruler to check each answer.

1. _____

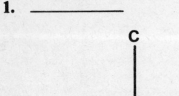

AB or CD

2. _____

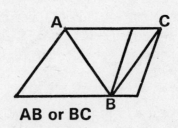

a or b

3. _____

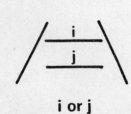

i or j

4. _____

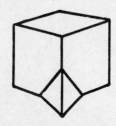

AB or BC

Right Angle Illusions

There are two right angles in the drawing that follows. See if you can spot them without measuring. Check your answers with a protractor or with the corner of a piece of paper.

5. _____

Parallel Line Illusions

In each drawing below, do the two horizontal center lines bow in, bow out, or are they parallel? Use a ruler to check the actual distance between the lines in each problem.

6. _____

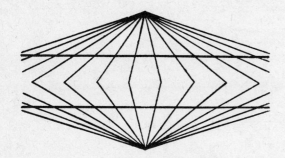

7. _____

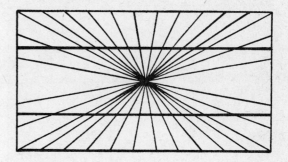

Area Illusions

In each drawing below, choose the circle that has the largest area.

8. _____

c or d

9. _____

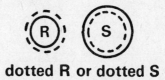

dotted R or dotted S

Volume Illusions

Which of the two rectangular solids drawn below has the greatest volume?

10. _____

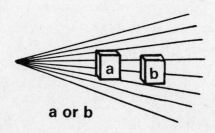

a or b

ANSWER KEY

Page 2

1. ∠ABC or ∠CBA
2. ∠a
3. ∠o
4. a) acute
5. c) obtuse
6. 135°
7. 60°

Page 3

8.

9.

10. ∠GHI = 19°
11. 53°
12. 76°
13. 32°

Page 4

14. ∠ABC = 61°
15. 54°
16. 42°
17. 102°
18. ∠2 = 30°, ∠3 = 150°, ∠4 = 30°
19. ∠a = 155°, ∠b = 155°, ∠c = 25°

Page 5

20.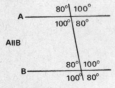

21.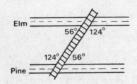

Page 7

1. c
2. f
3. h
4. j
5. o
6. q
7. a&b
8. d&e
9. g&i
10. j&l

Page 9

1. 20°
2. 120°
3. 200°
4. d) 35°
5. e) 90°
6. b) 150°
7. a) 180°
8. c) 210°
9. 30°
10. 40°
11. 90°
12. 180°

Page 11

1. acute
2. right
3. obtuse
4. straight
5. reflex
6. acute
7. obtuse
8. reflex
9. straight

Page 12

1. ∠CDE or ∠EDC
2. ∠F
3. ∠5
4. ∠M
5. ∠RST or ∠TSR
6. ∠b

Page 13

1. ∠ABC = 30°, acute
2. ∠DEF = 90°, right
3. ∠XYZ = 160°, obtuse
4. ∠RST = 180°, straight

Pages 14-15

5. ∠ABC = 50°, a) acute
6. ∠RST = 45°, a) acute
7. ∠DEF = 90°, b) right
8. ∠LMN = 90°, b) right
9. ∠XYZ = 125°, c) obtuse
10. ∠CDE = 160°, c) obtuse

Pages 16-17

1.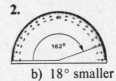

   c) stays the same

4.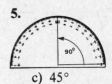

   d) 35° larger

2.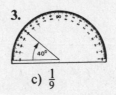

   b) 18° smaller

5.

   c) 45°

3.

   c) $\frac{1}{9}$

Page 19

1. ∠ABD = 60°
2. ∠TRS = 50°
3. ∠XYO = 32°
4. ∠MNP = 130°
5. ∠DBC = 143°
6. ∠OPT = 40°
7. ∠b = 140°, ∠c = 40°, ∠d = 140°
8. ∠1 = 75°, ∠3 = 75°, ∠4 = 105°
9. ∠a = 122°, ∠b = 58°, ∠c = 122°

Page 21

1. 40°
2. ∠1 = 132°, ∠2 = 48°, ∠3 = 132°
3. 98°
4. 90°, 90°, 90°
5. 33°
6. d) 45°
7. a) 180°
8. e) 135°
9. b) 90°
10. c) 360°

Page 23

1. 120° / 60°
    60° / 120°
    120° / 60°
    60° / 120°

3. 130° \ 50°
    50° \ 130°

2. 75° \ 105°
    105° \ 75°
    75° \ 105°
    105° \ 75°

4. 120°
    60°   60°
    120°

Page 24

1. 110°
2. 50°
3. 57°
4. 127°
5. 50°
6. 360°

Page 25

7. 120°
8. F, H, N, Z
9. ∠c
10. 60°
11. 35°
12. 52°

Page 26

1. ∠JKL or ∠LKJ
2. ∠D
3. ∠C
4. d) straight
5. c) obtuse
6. ∠FGH = 65°
7. ∠QRS = 150°

Page 27

8.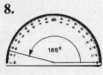
9.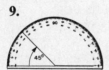

10. 56°
11. 30°
12. 19°
13. 10°

Page 28

14. 155°
15. 140°
16. 37°
17. 115°
18. ∠a = 125°, ∠b = 55°, ∠c = 125°
19. ∠1 = 128°, ∠2 = 52°, ∠3 = 128°

Page 29

20.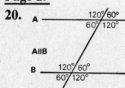
21.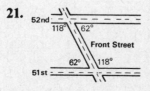

Page 30

1. 97°
2. 130°
3. 63°
4. d) scalene
5. e) "c" and "d" above

Page 31

6. x = 8
7. YZ = 24 in.
8. Yes
9. d = 32 yds.
10. 60 ft.
11. a) 9, b) 25, c) 49, d) 81

Page 32

12. a) 2, b) 6, c) 8, d) 10
13. 10 ft.
14. 13 ft.
15. 8 ft.

Page 35

1. △ ABC
2. △ LMN
3. △ RST
4. CD
5. GH
6. YZ
7. ∠D
8. ∠S
9. ∠B
10. ∠c
11. 12 ft.
12. ∠b
13. 8 ft.
14. ∠a
15. ∠b

Page 37

1. 52°
2. 86°
3. 32°
4. 37°
5. 62°
6. 68°
7. 31°
8. 19°
9. 116°
10. 83°
11. 55°
12. 104°

Pages 38-39

1. 42°
2. 23°
3. 28°
4. 96°
5. 119°
6. 55°
7. 60°
8. Yes

Page 42

1. Equilateral, each angle 60°
2. Isosceles, each base angle 71°
3. Scalene (and right —circled), 56°
4. Isosceles, vertex angle 54° and base angle 63°
5. Isosceles (and right —circled), each base angle 45°
6. Scalene, 20°
7. Scalene, 36°
8. Equilateral, each angle 60°
9. Isosceles, each base angle 55°
10. 17 mi.
11. 10 ft.
12. 39 m

Page 43

1. 50°
2. 55°
3. 95°
4. 60°
5. 45°
6. 60°
7. 131°
8. 34°

ANSWER KEY (continued)

Page 45
1. Yes, Because each triangle has the same three angles.
2. a) ∠L = ∠X, b) ∠M = ∠Y, c)∠N = ∠Z
3. a) LM and XY, b)MN and YZ, c) NL and ZX
4. △ FGH and △ IJK
5. No
6. Yes

Page 47
1. 9 in.
2. 4 in.
3. 20 in.
4. 8 ft.
5. 24 ft.
6. 30 mi.

Pages 48-49
1. $d = 24$ in.
2. $x = 60$ in.
3. $l = 9$ in.
4. $d = 24$ in.
5. $b = 36$ ft.
6. $x = 30$ in.
7. $s = 9$ in.
8. $l = 16$ ft.

Page 51
1. GH = 30 cm
2. GH = 9 ft.
3. OP = 9 mi.
4. QR = 12 yds.

Page 53
1. 24 ft.
2. 300 yds.
3. 70 ft.
4. 56 ft.

Page 54
1. 9
2. 64
3. 36
4. 81
5. 144
6. 100
7. 196
8. 225
9. 9
10. 49
11. 16
12. 289
13. 324
14. 169

Page 55
1. 49
2. 100
3. 9
4. 225
5. 64
6. 16
7. $b = 11$
8. $c = 5$
9. $x = 12$
10. $a = 1$
11. $d = 9$
12. $c = 2$
13. $x = 13$
14. $a = 6$
15. $b = 14$

Page 57
1. 5 in.
2. 13 in.
3. 15 yds.
4. 10 mi.
5. 13 ft.
6. 5 m

Page 59
1. 9 yds.
2. 4 yds.
3. 6 in.
4. 15 ft.
5. 12 in.
6. 8 cm

Pages 60-61
1. 13 ft.
2. 15 ft.
3. 10 in.
4. 15 ft.
5. 13 ft.
6. $9\frac{1}{2}$ yds.

Page 62
1. 27°
2. 22°
3. 42°
4. a) equilateral
5. b) isosceles
6. d = 30
7. CD = 25 ft

Page 63
8. No
9. 100 ft.
10. 30 ft.
11. a) 4, b) 16, c) 36, d) 64
12. a) 3, b) 6, c) 7, d) 9

Page 64
13. 5 ft.
14. 12 ft.
15. 10 ft.

Page 65
1. 16 ft. 11 in.
2. 18 m 15 cm
3. 4 yds. 2 ft.
4. 1 km 875 m
5. 69 yds.
6. 32 cm 4 mm
7. 1 yd. 2 ft.
8. No.
9. 9 ft. 4 in.

Page 66
10. Triangle
11. Square
12. Rectangle
13. Parallelogram
14. Trapezoid
15. Circle
16. 1) d 2) f
3) e 4) b
5) a 6) c

Page 67
17. P = 52 in., A = 169 sq. in.
18. P = 28 ft., A = 45 sq. ft.
19. P = 25 in., A = 21 sq. in.
20. P = 26 in., A = 35 sq. in.
21. P = 21 ft., A = 20 sq. ft.
22. C = 88 in., A = 616 sq. in.

Page 68
23. 112 m
24. 154 sq. ft.
25. 393 sq. ft.

Page 70
1. 156 in., 48 in.
2. 27 ft., 48 ft.
3. 21,120 ft., 10,560 ft.
4. 5,280 yds., 8,800 yds.

Page 71
5. 1 ft. 7 in., 2 ft. 7 in.
6. 3 yds. 2 ft., 2 yds. 2 ft.
7. 1 mi. 340 yds., 1 mi. 1,340 yds.
8. 7 ft. 5 in., 8 ft. 11 in.
9. 7 yds. 2 ft., 15 yds. 1 ft.
10. 2 mi. 2,720 ft., 2 mi. 5,000 ft.

Page 72

1. 90 mm, 40 mm, 60 mm
2. 700 cm, 900 cm, 500 cm
3. 7,000 m, 10,000 m, 4,000 m

Page 73

4. 7 cm 9 mm, 8 cm   6. 12 cm 7 mm,
   3 mm   12 cm 9 mm
5. 7 m 48 cm, 1 m   7. 13 m 56 cm, 20 m
   4 cm

Page 75

1. 9 ft. 1 in., 7 yds., 12 mi. 340 yds.
2. 12 yds. 2 ft., 16 ft. 8 in., 12 yds.
3. 11 cm 4 mm, 11 m 48 cm, 6 km 210 m
4. 28 m 90 cm, 45 cm 7 mm, 11 km 350 m
5. 2 ft. 7 in., 1 yd. 2 ft., 2 ft. 8 in.
6. 4 yds. 2 ft., 1 ft. 5 in., 2 ft.
7. 7 cm 9 mm, 17 m 65 cm, 5 km 650 m

Page 77

1. 60 ft., 38 yds. 2 ft., 15 mi. 1,040 yds.
2. 74 yds. 2 ft., 29 ft. 6 in., 24 yds.
3. 65 cm 8 mm, 19 cm, 29 m 80 cm
4. 2 ft. 5 in., 2 ft. 5 in., 2 ft. 3 in.
5. 3 yds. 1 ft., 4 yds. 2 ft., 9 yds. 2 ft.
6. 2 cm 7 mm, 1 m 80 cm, 1 km 260 m

Page 78

1. No   4. $1,458.00
2. Yes   5. 10 in.
3. 74 ft. 3 in.   6. 12 yds. 2 ft.

Page 79

7. Fred   11. 1 ft. 5 in.
8. 8 in.   12. 29 ft.
9. 24 km 275 m   13. 1 ft. 9 in.
10. 40 ft. 6 in. 14. 2 m 50 cm

Pages 80-81

1. 40 in. or 3 ft. 4 in.   5. 20 ft. 4 in.
2. 24 yds.   6. 42 yds. 2 ft.
3. 58 cm   7. 10 m 77 cm
4. 35 ft. or 11 yds. 2 ft. 8. 16 mi. 920 ft.

Page 83

1. Rectangle   7. Parallelogram
2. Triangle   8. Trapezoid
3. Square   9. Trapezoid
4. Rectangle   10. Triangle
5. Trapezoid   11. Rectangle
6. Rectangle   12. Trapezoid

Page 84

1. 12   3. 6   5. 7
2. 9   4. 8   6. 6

Page 85

7. 4½   10. 9   13. 28 or 29
8. 6   11. 9   14. about 25
9. 7½   12. 7

Page 87

1. 28 in. or 2 ft. 4 in.   7. 68 yds.
2. 36 yds.   8. 17 ft. 4 in.
3. 49 ft. 8 in.   9. 10 times
4. 84 m   10. 41 ft. or 13 yds. 2 ft.
5. 72 in. or 6 ft.   11. 110 yds.
6. 22 cm 8 mm   12. 22 ft. or 7 yds. 1 ft.

Page 89

1. 81 sq. ft.   5. 64 sq. ft.
2. 8 cm   6. 3 ft.
3. 20.25 sq. in.   7. 289 sq. yds.
4. 900 cm²   8. 64 tiles

Page 90

1. 26 yds.   3. 14 ft. 2 in.
2. 68 ft. or 22 yds. 2 ft.

Page 91

4. 40 m 90 cm   9. 23 ft. 4 in.
5. 23 yds. 1 ft.   10. 5
6. 10 ft. 8 in.   11. 167 m 50 cm
7. 71 ft.   12. 44 ft. 11 in.
8. 168 in. or 14 ft.

Page 93

1. 117 sq. ft.   7. 22½ sq. yds.
2. 7 km²   8. 640 sq. ft.
3. 8 in.   9. 75 ft.
4. 9 sq. ft.   10. No
5. 9.1 cm   11. 9 sq. ft.
6. 4,000 sq. yds.   12. 50 m

Page 94

1. 28 in. or 2 ft. 4 in.   4. 5 mi. 740 yds.
2. 14 ft. 3 in.   5. 31 m 45 cm
3. 28 cm 4 mm   6. 14 yds. 1 ft.

ANSWER KEY (continued)

Page 95

7. 83 yds.
8. 75 ft. 8 in.
9. 564 m
10. 33 in. or 2 ft. 9 in.
11. 4
12. 23 cm 2 mm
13. 23 ft. 9 in.
14. 1 ft. 6 in.

Page 97

1. 56 sq. in.
2. $22\frac{1}{2}$ sq. yds.
3. $7\frac{1}{2}$ cm^2
4. $8\frac{1}{4}$ sq. ft.
5. 25 sq. ft.
6. $4\frac{1}{2}$ sq. yds.

Page 99

1. 8 cm 2 mm
2. 26 ft
3. 6 ft. 2 in.
4. 13 ft. 8 in.
5. 21 km 100 m
6. 21 ft. 8 in.
7. 16 ft. 2 in.
8. 284 m 15 cm
9. 278 ft.
10. 4
11. 5 m 92 cm
12. 5 ft. 4 in.

Page 101

1. 35 sq. in.
2. 30 m^2
3. 110 sq. ft.
4. 792 sq. ft.
5. 945 m^2
6. 24

Page 102

1. 88 in.
2. 16.0 ft.
3. 176 m

Page 103

4. $15\frac{5}{7}$ ft.
5. 10.7 m
6. $18\frac{6}{7}$ mi.
7. $12\frac{4}{7}$ mi.
8. 1.3 mi.
9. $37\frac{5}{7}$ ft.
10. 44 cm
11. 14.1 ft.
12. 44 m

Page 104

1. 616 sq. in.
2. 116.8 sq. ft.
3. 1,386 km^2
4. 154 m^2
5. $78\frac{4}{7}$ sq. in.
6. 8.0 sq. yds.

Page 105

7. $452\frac{4}{7}$ sq. in.
8. 616 sq. ft.
9. 30.2 m^2
10. 26 sq. in.
11. 616 sq. ft.
12. 22,176 km^2

Page 107

1. 17 ft. 2 in., 15 sq. ft.
2. 26 km, 36 km^2
3. 34 in., 60 sq. in.
4. $25\frac{1}{2}$ yds., 15 sq. yds.
5. $31\frac{3}{7}$ cm, $78\frac{4}{7}$ cm^2
6. 18 in., 18 sq. in.
7. 20.1 ft., 32.2 sq. ft.
8. 8 cm 1 mm, 3 cm^2
9. 12 ft., 9 sq. ft.

Page 108

10. $12\frac{4}{7}$ sq. ft.
11. $78.75
12. 3,381 yds. 1 ft. or almost 2 mi.
13. 880 ft.
14. 136 sq. ft.
15. 38.5 m^2
16. 1,310 yds.
17. 154 ft.

Page 109

18. 441 m^2
19. 600 sq. ft.
20. 40 yds. 2 ft.
21. 1,386 sq. ft.
22. 1,800 sq.ft.
23. d) $\frac{1}{2}$
24. b) 5
25. 64 m 30 cm

Page 111

1. 192 sq. ft.
2. 261 sq. ft.
3. $304\frac{1}{2}$ sq. ft.
4. 329 sq. ft.

Page 112

1. 67 sq. ft.
2. 177 sq. ft

Page 113

3. 6,070 sq. ft.
4. 246 sq. ft.
5. 42 cm^2
6. 400 sq. ft.

Page 114

1. 19 yds. 2 ft.
2. 19 cm 9 mm
3. 3 ft. 9 in.
4. 20 m 94 cm
5. 12 m 25 cm
6. 2 ft. 5 in.
7. 1 m 28 cm
8. 1 ft. 10 in.
9. 5 ft. 8 in.
10. Trapezoid
11. Circle
12. Triangle
13. Parallelogram
14. Rectangle
15. Square

Page 115

16. 1) c, 2) e, 3) a, 4) f, 5) b, 6) d
17. 39 ft., 77 sq. ft.
18. 20 in., 25 sq. in.
19. 44 in., 154 sq. in.
20. $31\frac{1}{2}$ ft., $49\frac{1}{2}$ sq. ft.
21. 98 yds., 490 sq. yds.
22. 48 mi., $103\frac{1}{2}$ sq. mi.

Page 116

23. 44 ft.
24. 1,225 m^2
25. 524 sq. ft.
26. 99 sq. ft.

Page 118

1. 1) c, 2) d, 3) a, 4) b
2. 280 cu. in.
3. 510 cu. yds.
4. $12\frac{4}{7}$ cu. ft.
5. 1,078 cm^3

Page 119

6. 1,000 cu. ft.
7. 10,500 m^3
8. 9,240 cu. ft.
9. $104\frac{16}{21}$ cu. yds.
10. 777 cu. in.
11. $262\frac{2}{7}$ cu. in.

Page 121

1. Cylinder
2. Cube
3. Rectangular Solid
4. Cone
5. Cylinder
6. Rectangular Solid
7. Cube
8. Rectangular Solid
9. Cone
10. Rectangular Solid
11. Cone
12. Cylinder

Page 123

1. 64
2. 45
3. 27
4. 42
5. 15
6. 20

Page 125

1. 343 cu. in.
2. 27 cm³
3. 512 cu. yds.
4. 5,832 cu. yds.
5. 27 m³
6. 68.921 metric tons
7. 112
8. 125

Page 126

1. 192 cu. ft.
2. 252 cu. yds.
3. 1,120 cm³

Page 127

4. 350 cu. in.
5. 30 cu. in.
6. 36 m³
7. 15 cu. ft.
8. 12 cu. ft.
9. 30 m³
10. 20 cu. ft.

Page 128

1. 22 m³
2. $942\frac{6}{7}$ cu. in.
3. 307.7 cu. ft.

Page 129

1. $4,106\frac{2}{3}$ cu. ft.
2. $2\frac{2}{21}$ cu. ft.
3. 19.6 cm³

Pages 130-131

1. 40 cu. ft.
2. 1,540 cu. ft.
3. 264 m³
4. $26\frac{2}{3}$ cu. yds.
5. 125 cu. ft.
6. $209\frac{11}{21}$ cu. ft.
7. $9\frac{3}{7}$ m³
8. 49.4 cu. yds.
9. 1 cm³
10. 49.5 cu. in.

Page 133

1. 518 cu. ft.
2. 2,220 cu. in.
3. 1,302.9 cu. in.
4. $3,593\frac{1}{3}$ cm³

Pages 134-135

1. 180 cu. in.
2. 24 cu. ft.
3. 168 cu. in.
4. $722\frac{6}{7}$ cm³
5. 308 cu. ft.
6. 3,150 cu. in.

Page 136

1. Cube
2. Cylinder
3. Cone
4. 1) c, 2) a, 3) d, 4) b
5. 216 cu. ft.
6. 165 cu. in.

Page 137

7. 3,080 cu. yds.
8. 18,018 cu. in.
9. 27 cu. yds.
10. 1,120 cu. ft.
11. 61,600 cu. ft.
12. $513\frac{1}{3}$ cu. yds.

Page 138

13. 156 cu. ft.
14. $691\frac{3}{7}$ cu. in.

Page 139

1. 90°
2. 45°
3. 55°
4. 145°

Page 140

5. 75°
6. 105°
7. 124°
8. 99°
9. 15 yds.

Page 141

10. 75 ft.
11. 13 mi.
12. 8 m
13. 8 ft. 8 in.
14. 20 sq. yds.
15. 14 cm²

Page 142

16. b) πr^2
17. 84 sq. ft.
18. d) $\frac{11}{14}$

Pages 143-144

19. 5,006 sq. ft.
20. 70 cu. ft.
21. e) $\pi r^2 h$
22. 462 cu. ft.
23. 9 sections
24. 12 cu. in.

Pages 146-147

1. a) 17 ft., b) Yes
2. a) 20 ft., b) No, it is not.
3. B   Smaller Work Triangle.
4. a) Equilateral, b) 4 ft.

Pages 148-149

1. 100 ft.
2. 45 mi.
3. 46 mi.
4. 26 hrs.
5. 44 mi.
6. No
7. 243 ft.

Pages 150-151

1. a) 208 tiles
   b) $166.40
   c) $175.00
   d) 142
2. a) $125
   b) 52 tiles
3. a) 270 sq. ft.
   b) 480
   c) $360.00
   d) 7
   e) $42.00
   f) $402.00

ANSWER KEY (continued)

Page 152

1. a) L = 7 yds., W = 5 yds., T = $\frac{1}{9}$ yd.
   b) $3\frac{8}{9}$ cu. yds.
   c) $280
   d) $472.50

Page 153

2. a) $3\frac{1}{3}$ cu. yds.
   b) $230
   c) 6 months

3. a) 3 cu. yds.
   b) $216
   c) 38 bricks
   d) $30.02

Page 154

1. a) L = $4\frac{1}{3}$ yds., W = 4 yds.
   b) $17\frac{1}{3}$ sq. yds.
   c) $260

2. $189

Page 155

3. a) $14\frac{2}{3}$ sq. yds.
   b) $205.33
   c) 11 sq. ft.

4. a) $312
   b) 25 sq. ft.

Pages 156-157

1. a) 4,096 sq. ft., b) about 6 bags, c) $22.80
2. a) 11 rosebushes, b) $76.45, c) $39.16
3. a) 600 sq. ft., b) $165.00, c) $138.03

Page 159

1. $22\frac{1}{2}$ gallons

2. almost 8 days

3. a) 15 cu. ft., b) $112\frac{1}{2}$ gallons, c) $937\frac{1}{2}$ lbs.
4. No. The tank holds about 93 gallons.

Page 161

1. $\frac{2}{5}$ in.
2. a) 10 ft., b) $\frac{2}{5}$ in.

3. a) 7 in., b) $\frac{5}{7}$ in.

Pages 162-163

1.-4. All line segments are same lengths.
5.

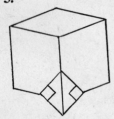

6.-7. Both sets of lines are parallel.
8.-9. Each circle is same size.
10. Both solids are same size.